α Alpha

Focus: Single-Digit Addition and Subtraction

Instruction Manual

Canadian Edition

By Steven P. Demme

Math·U·See

1-888-854-MATH (6284)
www.MathUSee.ca

 # Math·U·See

1-888-854-MATH (6284)

www.MathUSee.ca

Copyright © 2010 by Steven P. Demme

Graphic Design by Christine Minnich
Illustrations by Gregory Snader

Printed in Canada

α Alpha

Math·U·See

SCOPE & SEQUENCE

Math-U-See is a complete and comprehensive K-12 math curriculum. While each book focuses on a specific theme, Math-U-See continuously reviews and integrates topics and concepts presented in previous levels.

Primer

α Alpha | Focus: Single-Digit Addition and Subtraction

β Beta | Focus: Multiple-Digit Addition and Subtraction

γ Gamma | Focus: Multiplication

δ Delta | Focus: Division

ε Epsilon | Focus: Fractions

ζ Zeta | Focus: Decimals and Percents

Pre-Algebra

Algebra 1

Stewardship*

Geometry

Algebra 2

PreCalculus with Trigonometry

Calculus

*Stewardship is a biblical approach to personal finance. The requisite knowledge for this curriculum is a mastery of the four basic operations, as well as fractions, decimals, and percents. In the Math-U-See sequence these topics are thoroughly covered in Alpha through Zeta. We also recommend Pre-Algebra and Algebra 1 since over half of the lessons require some knowledge of algebra. Stewardship may be studied as a one-year math course or in conjunction with any of the secondary math levels.

HOW TO USE

Five Minutes for Success

Welcome to *Alpha*. I believe you will have a positive experience with the unique Math-U-See approach to teaching math. These first few pages explain the essence of this methodology, which has worked for thousands of students and teachers. I hope you will take five minutes and read through these steps carefully.

The student should be able to count and write the numbers from zero to nine, and be ready for formal schooling.

If you are using the program properly and still need additional help, you may contact your Canadian representative, or visit us online at mathusee.ca/support.

— Steve Demme

The Goal of Math-U-See

The underlying assumption or premise of Math-U-See is that the reason we study math is to apply math in everyday situations. Our goal is to help produce confident problem solvers who enjoy the study of math. These are students who learn their math facts, rules, and formulas and are able to use this knowledge to solve word problems and real-life applications. Therefore, the study of math is much more than simply committing to memory a list of facts. It includes memorization, but it also encompasses learning the underlying concepts of math that are critical to successful problem solving.

More than Memorization

Many people confuse memorization with understanding. Once while I was teaching seven junior high students, I asked how many pieces they would each receive if there were fourteen pieces. The students' response was, "What do we do: add, subtract, multiply, or divide?" Knowing **how** to divide is important; understanding **when** to divide is equally important.

THE SUGGESTED 4-STEP MATH-U-SEE APPROACH

In order to train students to be confident problem solvers, here are the four steps that I suggest you use to get the most from the Math-U-See curriculum.

Step 1. Prepare for the Lesson
Step 2. Present the New Topic
Step 3. Practice for Mastery
Step 4. Progression after Mastery

Step 1. Prepare for the Lesson

Watch the DVD to learn the new concept and see how to demonstrate this concept with the manipulatives when applicable. Study the written explanations and examples in the instruction manual. Many students watch the DVD along with their instructor.

Step 2. Present the New Topic

Present the new concept to your student. Have the student watch the DVD with you, if you think it would be helpful.

a. Build: Use the manipulatives to demonstrate the problems from the worksheet.

b. Write: Record the step-by-step solutions on paper as you work them through with manipulatives.

c. Say: Explain the *why* and *what* of math as you build and write.

Do as many problems as you feel are necessary until the student is comfortable with the new material. One of the joys of teaching is hearing a student say, *"Now I get it!"* or *"Now I see it!"*

Step 3. Practice for Mastery

Using the examples and the lesson practice problems from the student text, have the students practice the new concept until they understand it. It is one thing for students to watch someone else do a problem; it is quite another to do the same problem themselves. Do enough examples together until they can do them without assistance.

Do as many of the lesson practice pages as necessary (not all of the pages may be needed) until the students remember the new material and gain understanding. Give special attention to the word problems, which are designed to apply the concept being taught in the lesson.

Another resource is the Math-U-See web site, which has online drill and downloadable worksheets for more practice. To find them, go to www.MathUSee.ca and select "E-Sources."

Step 4. Progression after Mastery

Once mastery of the new concept is demonstrated, proceed to the systematic review pages for that lesson. Mastery can be demonstrated by having each student teach the new material back to you. The goal is not to fill in worksheets, but to be able to teach back what has been learned.

The systematic review worksheets review the new material as well as provide practice of the math concepts previously studied. Remediate missed problems as they arise to ensure continued mastery. If you wish, you may use the "extra fun" sheets in the test and activity booklet to enrich the lessons.

Proceed to the lesson tests. These were designed to be an assessment tool to help determine mastery, but they may also be used as extra worksheets. Your students will be ready for the next lesson only after demonstrating mastery of the new concept and continued mastery of concepts found in the systematic review worksheets.

Confucius is reputed to have said, "Tell me, I forget; Show me, I understand; Let me do it, I will remember." To which we add, **"Let me teach it and I will have achieved mastery!"**

Length of a Lesson

So how long should a lesson take? This will vary from student to student and from topic to topic. You may spend a day on a new topic, or you may spend several days. There are so many factors that influence this process that it is impossible to predict the length of time from one lesson to another. I have spent three days on a lesson and I have also invested three weeks in a lesson. This occurred in the same book with the same student. If you move from lesson to lesson too quickly without the student demonstrating mastery, he will become overwhelmed and discouraged as he is exposed to more new material without having learned the previous topics. But if you move too slowly, your student may become bored and lose interest in math. I believe that as you regularly spend time working along with your student, you will sense when is the right time to take the lesson test and progress through the book.

By following the four steps outlined above, you will have a much greater opportunity to succeed. Math must be taught sequentially, as it builds line upon line and precept upon precept on previously learned material. I hope you will try this methodology and move at your student's pace. As you do, I think you will be helping to create a confident problem solver who enjoys the study of math.

ONGOING SUPPORT
AND ADDITIONAL RESOURCES

Welcome to the Math-U-See Family!

Now that you have invested in your children's education, I would like to tell you about the resources that are available to you. Allow me to introduce you to our staff, our ever-improving website, the Math-U-See Blog, our free e-mail newsletter, and other online resources.

Many of our customer service representatives have been with us for over 10 years. What makes them unique is their desire to serve and their expertise. They are able to answer your questions, place your student(s) in the appropriate level, and provide knowledgeable support throughout the school year.

Come to your local curriculum fair where you can meet us face-to-face, see the latest products, attend a workshop, meet other MUS users at the booth, and be refreshed. We are at most curriculum fairs and events. To find the fair nearest you, click on "Events" under "E-sources."

The **Website**, at www.MathUSee.ca, is continually being updated and improved. It has many excellent tools to enhance your teaching and provide more practice for your student(s).

 **ONLINE DRILL**
Let your students review their math facts online. Just enter the facts you want to learn and start drilling. This is a great way to commit those facts to memory.

WORKSHEET GENERATOR
Create custom worksheets to print out and use with your students. It's easy to use and gives you the flexibility to focus on a specific lesson. Best of all — it's free!

Math-U-See Blog

Interesting insights and up-to-date information appear regularly on the Math-U-See Blog. The blog features updates, rep highlights, fun pictures, and stories from other users. Visit us and get the latest scoop on what is happening .

Email Newsletter

For the latest news and practical teaching tips, sign up online for the free Math-U-See e-mail newsletter. Each month you will receive an e-mail with a teaching tip from Steve as well as the latest news from the website. It's short, beneficial, and fun. Sign up today!

Online Support

You will find a variety of helpful tools on our website, including corrections lists, placement tests, answers to questions, and support options.

For Specific Math Help

When you have watched the DVD instruction and read the instruction manual and still have a question, we are here to help. Call us or click the support link. Our trained staff are available to answer a question or walk you through a specific lesson.

Feedback

Send us an e-mail by clicking the feedback link. We are here to serve you and help you teach math. Ask a question, leave a comment, or tell us how you and your student are doing with Math-U-See.

Our hope and prayer is that you and your students will be equipped to have a successful experience with math!

Blessings,

Steve Demme

LESSON 1

Place Value and the Manipulatives

Two skills are necessary to function in the *decimal system*: the ability to count from zero to nine, and an understanding of *place value*. In the decimal system, where everything is based on ten (deci), you count to nine and then start over. To illustrate this, count the following numbers slowly: 800, 900, 1000. We read these as eight hundred, nine hundred, one thousand. Now read these: 80, 90, 100. Notice how you count from one to nine and then begin again. These are read as eighty, ninety, one hundred. Once you can count to nine, you can begin work on place value.

The two keys are learning the counting numbers zero through nine, which tell us how many; and understanding place value, which tells us what kind.

COUNTING

When counting, begin with zero and then proceed to nine. Traditionally we've started with one and counted to ten. Look at the two charts that follow and see which is more logical.

```
 1  2  3  4  5  6  7  8  9 10      0  1  2  3  4  5  6  7  8  9
11 12 13 14 15 16 17 18 19 20     10 11 12 13 14 15 16 17 18 19
21 22 23 24 25 26 27 28 29 30     20 21 22 23 24 25 26 27 28 29
```

The second chart has all single digits in the first line; then, in the second line, each is preceded by a one in the tens place. The next line has a two preceding each number instead of a one. The first chart, though more familiar, has the 10, the 20, and the 30 in the wrong lines. When counting, always begin with zero and count to nine and then start over.

PLACE VALUE

I define this important subject as "Every value has its own place!" To an older child I would add, "Place determines value!" Both are true. There are ten symbols to tell you how many, and many values to represent what kind or what value. The numbers zero through nine tell us how many; *units*, *tens*, and *hundreds* tell us what kind. For the sake of accuracy, we will use units rather than ones to denote the first value. One is a counting number that tells us how many, and units is a place value that denotes what kind. This will save potential confusion when saying "ten ones" or "one ten." Remember, one is a number and units is a place value. The numerals (0–9) tell us how many tens, how many hundreds, or how many units. We begin our study focusing on the units, tens, and hundreds, but there are other place values such as thousands, millions, billions, and so on.

When teaching place value, I like to illustrate it by using a street, since I'm talking about a place. I call the street Decimal Street and have the little green units house, the tall blue tens house next door, and the huge red hundreds castle beside the tens. We don't want to forget what we learned from counting—that we count only to nine and then start over. To make this more real, begin by asking, "What is the largest number of units that can live in this house?" You can get any response to this question, from zero to nine, and you might say "yes" to all of them, but remind the student that the largest number is nine! So we imagine how many little green beds, or green toothbrushes, or green chairs there would be in the house. Ask the student what else there would be nine of. Do the same with the tens and the hundreds. Remember that in these houses all the furniture will be blue (tens) and red (hundreds).

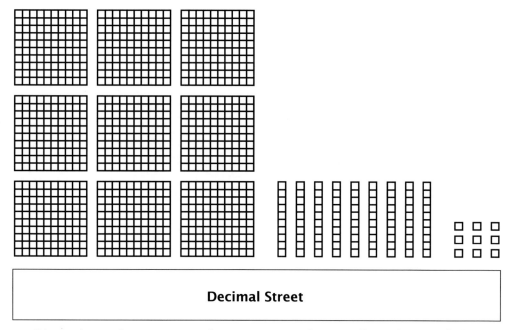

Decimal Street

Throughout the program, whenever we teach we will employ the following strategy: Build, Write, Verbalize. To teach place value, we will first build the number and then count how many in each place. Finally, write the number and read what we've written.

Let's build 142 (1 hundred, 4 tens, 2 units). Now count how many are "home" at each house. I like to imagine going up to the door of each home and knocking to see how many are home in each place. Write the numerals 1 4 2 as you count (always beginning with the units) to show the value on paper. Then say, "One hundred four tens and two units, or one hundred forty-two." Build another example and have the student write how many are home. When they understand this, write the number on paper and have them build it. Try 217. After they build it, read what they have built. Keep practicing, with the teacher building and the student writing, and vice versa.

Here is another exercise I do to reinforce the fact that every value has its own place. I like to have the student close his/her eyes as I move the pieces around by placing the red hundreds where the units should be and vice versa. I then ask the student to make sure they are all in the right place. You might call this "scramble the values" or "walk the blocks home." As the student looks at the problem and begins to work on it, I ask, "Is every value in its own place?"

An important symbol that I haven't mentioned is Mr. Zero (0). He is a place holder. Let's say you were walking down Decimal Street and knocking on each door to see who was home. If you knock on the Units door and three Units answer, you have three in the units place. Next door, at the Tens house, you knock and no one answers! Yet you know someone is there feeding the goldfish and taking care of the bird, as a housesitter might when a family goes on vacation. Mr. Zero won't answer the door because he's not a Ten; he's the one who holds their place until the Tens come home. Upon knocking at the Hundreds big red castle, you find two Hundreds answer the door. Thus your numeral is 203.

At some point you will want to mention that even though we begin at the units end of the street and proceed right to left from the units to the hundreds, when we read numbers we do it left to right. We want to get into the habit of counting units first, so when we add, we will add units first, then tens, and then hundreds.

Remember, we teach with the blocks, and then we move to the worksheets once the student understands the new material.

You've probably noticed the important relationship between language and place value.

Consider 142, read as one hundred forty-two. We know that it is made up of one red hundred square (one hundred) and four blue ten bars (forty—*ty* for ten) and two units. The hundreds are very clear and self-explanatory, but the tens are where we need to focus our attention.

When pronouncing 90, 80, 70, 60, and 40, work on enunciating clearly so that 90 is ninety, not "ninedee." 80 is eighty, not "adee." When you pronounce the numbers accurately, not only will your spelling improve, but your understanding of place value as well. Seventy (70) is seven tens and sixty (60) is six tens. Forty (40) is pronounced correctly but spelled without the *u*. Carrying through on this logic, 50 should be pronounced "five-ty" instead of fifty. Thirty and twenty are similar to fifty, not completely consistent but close enough so we know what they mean. The teens are the real problem. Some researchers have concluded that one of the chief differences between Western (American and Canadian) and Eastern (Chinese and Japanese) students is their understanding of place value.

The culprit, in the researchers' eyes, is the English language. In Eastern culture, when a child can count to nine, with a few minor variations he can count to one hundred. Not so in English, with such numbers as ten, eleven, twelve and the rest of the teens. Not only are these numbers difficult to teach, because there seems to be no rhyme nor reason as to their origin, but more importantly, they do not reflect and indicate place value. To remedy this serious deficiency, I'm suggesting a new way to read the numbers 10 through 19. You decide whether this method reinforces the place value concept and restores logic and order to the decimal system. Ten is "onety," 11 is "onety-one," 12 is "onety-two," 13 is "onety-three," and so on. Now, it is not that students can't say ten, eleven, and twelve but that learning this method enhances their understanding and makes math logical again. Also, children think it is neat.

When presenting place value or any other topic in this curriculum, model how you think as you solve the problems. When you as the teacher work through a problem with the manipulatives, do it verbally so that as the student observes, he or she also hears your thinking process. Then record your answer.

Example 1

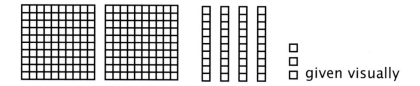 given visually

As you look at the picture, say it slowly, proceeding from left to right: "two hundred forty-three." Then count, beginning with the units, "1-2-3," and write a 3 in the units place. Then count the tens, "1-2-3-4," and write a 4 in the tens place. Finally, count the hundreds, "1-2," and write a 2 in the hundreds place. Do several of these, and then give the student the opportunity to do some.

Many students have been taught to write an "open" four, while most printed material has a "closed" four. Either way is correct. Just be sure that the student recognizes both styles.

Example 2
274 (given in writing)

Read the number two hundred seventy-four, and then say two hundreds as you pick up two red hundred squares. Then say seven-ty or seven tens and pick up seven blue ten bars. Say four and pick up four green unit pieces. Place them in the correct places as you repeat, "Every value has its own place."

Example 3
"one hundred sixty-five" (given verbally)

Read the number slowly, and then say one hundred as you pick up one red hundred square. Then say six-ty or six tens and pick up six blue ten bars. Now say five and pick up five green unit pieces. Place them in the correct place as you say, "Every value has its own place." Finally, write the number 165.

Do several problems each way (in writing and verbally), and then give the student the opportunity to do some.

Game for Place Value

Pick a Card - Make a set of cards with the numerals 0 through 9 written in green, one numeral on each card. Then make another stack of cards with the same numerals written in blue. (You may use the cards from the extra activity pages in the test and activity book if you wish.) Create one more stack of cards with the numerals 0 through 9 written in red. Shuffle the green cards, pick one, and display that number of green unit blocks. If a child picks a green 4, then count out four green unit blocks and display them.

When the child is proficient at this game, try it with the blue cards and do the same thing except choose the blue ten blocks instead of the green unit blocks. When he can do the tens well, combine the green cards and the blue cards. Have the child choose one card from the green pile and one card from the blue pile and pick up the correct number of blue ten blocks and green unit blocks. When he or she is an expert at this, add the red cards and proceed as before. Place them in three stacks, shuffle, and draw from each stack. Have the student show you with the blocks what number he has drawn.

Get a large piece of paper for a background, and cut out three houses. The units house should be green and 4 cm x 4 cm. The tens house should be blue and 11 cm x 12.5 cm. The hundreds house should be red and 38 cm x 38 cm. Each of these should be able to hold exactly nine of each piece. This drawing is not to scale.

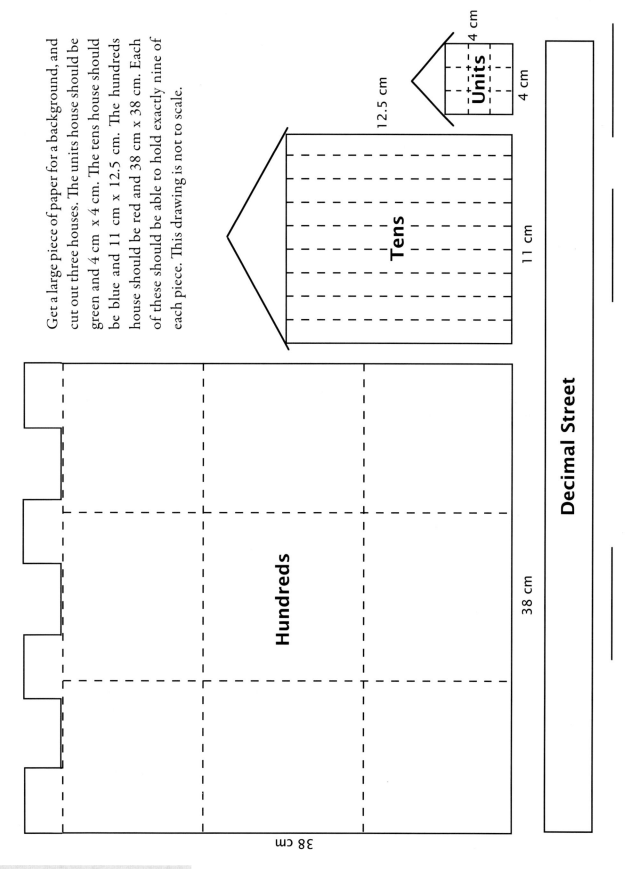

4 cm

4 cm

Units

12.5 cm

Tens

11 cm

Hundreds

38 cm

38 cm

Decimal Street

LESSON 2

Counting to 20

The transition from 9 to 10 is pivotal in understanding counting to 100 and regrouping (carrying).

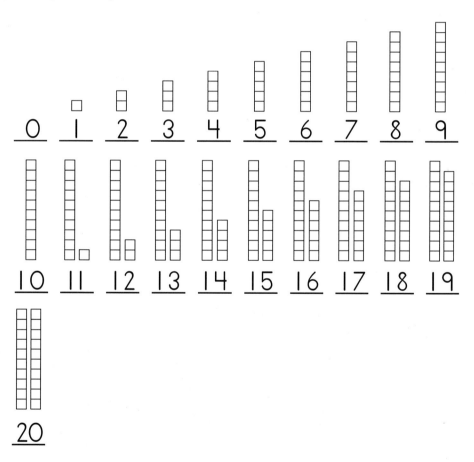

On the worksheets, the students practice writing their numbers on the lines that correspond to the pictures above. I left in a few numbers just to make the practice more interesting.

___ 1 ___ 3 4 ___ ___ 7 ___ 9

10 ___ ___ ___ ___ 15 16 ___ 18 ___

20

Notice that the student sheets have both regular and open fours (see above). Open fours are usually easier for students to write. Your student should recognize fours and ones in both the handwritten and printed forms and know that both forms mean the same thing.

Another way to teach counting to 20 uses the first two houses in Decimal Street, which is used in lesson 1 to introduce place value. Begin by placing one green unit block in the units house and saying and writing 1. Add another unit block and say and write 2. Keep doing this procedure until there are 9 at home in the units house. Then try to add one more and notice that there is no more room. The dry math reality at this point is that the 10 individual green units are transformed into a blue ten bar. To make it more interesting, we can make up a story about these new units who keep moving into our neighbourhood.

Apparently they heard that we have a nice home, and naturally they want to live with us. After we welcome them into our home, we find that we like them as well. So when the house is full (nine units), and a new fellow wants to live with us, we have a family discussion. We decide that in order for him to live with us, we will all have to become a blue ten bar and move into the house next door, so we can all be together.

As more units arrive, they can stay in the units house because it is now open. When the first unit arrives after we have moved into the tens house, we have one ten bar and one unit bar, or 11. The next one arrives and there are 12—one ten and two units—living on our street. Eventually we have 19 units. When the next one arrives, another 10 is formed and moves in with the original 10, so now there are two tens, or 20. This is illustrated on the next page.

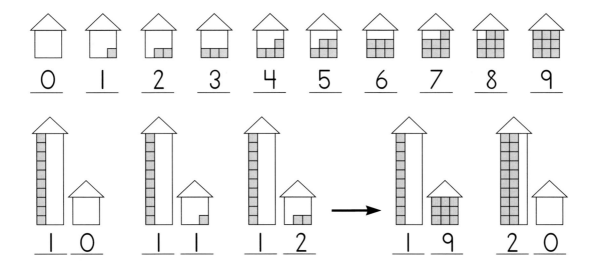

When counting to 20, encourage the students to count aloud using the nicknames: "one, two . . . eight, nine, ten, eleven, twelve . . . twenty," as well as with the proper names: "eight, nine, onety, onety-one, onety-two . . . two-ty." The nicknames are used most often, but the proper names help the student comprehend place value.

LESSON 3

Unit Bars

Now we will wean the student from the green units. When teaching place value, I use the red, blue, and green blocks. However, before attempting addition, be sure that the student knows that a group of three green units is the same as one pink unit bar, which is three units long. Place the blocks side by side to teach this. Show that the three individual green units "glued together" are the same length as the three bar.

The skill we are teaching here is often called the conservation of matter. Young children would rather have five pennies than one nickel. Their brains have developed to the next level when they know that five pennies and one nickel have the same value. This concept is very important, as it is the basis of addition—two units plus three units have the same value as five units. So we wean the student from using the green units exclusively to using the coloured units bars as well. On the worksheet, match the units on the left with the correct bar on the right. You can have the student colour the bars on the right to match the blocks.

There are four levels of combining or arithmetic:

1. Counting

2. Adding, which is fast counting

3. Multiplying, which is fast adding

4. Exponents, which are fast multiplying

To move from counting to adding, the student has to learn the values of the bars so that we can add two plus three and get five, instead of counting, "one, two," and then, "three, four, five."

Word = # = Unit pieces   **Unit Bar and Colour**

Two = 2 = □ □   = ☐☐
Orange

Three = 3 = □ □ □   = ☐☐☐
Pink

Four = 4 = □ □ □ □   = ☐☐☐☐
Yellow

Five = 5 = □ □ □ □ □   = ☐☐☐☐☐
Light Blue

Six = 6 = □□□ / □□□   = ☐☐☐☐☐☐
Violet or Purple

Seven = 7 = □□□□ / □□□   = ☐☐☐☐☐☐☐
Tan or Vanilla

Eight = 8 = □□□□ / □□□□   = ☐☐☐☐☐☐☐☐
Brown

Nine = 9 = □□□□□ / □□□□   = ☐☐☐☐☐☐☐☐☐
Light Green

Games for Unit Bar Identification

Simon Says - Examples: "Put a three on your nose," or "Hide two fives in a pocket."

What's Missing? - Put the one through nine blocks on the table. Ask the student to cover his eyes while you remove one of the blocks, and then ask him which one is missing. Take turns. There are numerous options to this. Try removing two blocks, or start with two of each number and remove one or two blocks.

The Grab Bag - Put the one through nine blocks in an opaque bag. Take turns either drawing a number card and finding a particular block, or telling each other to feel around and find a certain block. The easier version is to simply name the one you are about to pull out. A harder version would be to name the missing block after one has been removed.

Blocks and Symbols Match-Up - Make a set of cards with the symbols 1 through 9 on them (or use the cards from the activity pages in the test booklet). On the back of the cards draw a coloured dot to match the blocks. Place the cards symbol side up and match the blocks to them. This is especially good as a shelf activity that the student can get out on his own. It is self-correcting. Go ahead and let them peek; they stop soon enough. Introduce the symbols by doing the first three, then the next three, and finally all nine.

Sing and Grab - "If you're happy and you know it" . . . "Clap three times," or "Grab a five," etc.

Teaching Tip

As you get ready to begin teaching the addition facts, be sure to give the student time to "play" with the blocks. Some schools schedule a portion of each day for "play" and refer to this time as "free exploration."

As the student builds, he automatically learns the relationships between the different numbers. For example, if a six bar is laid on top of a ten bar, it doesn't take long for most students to realize that a four bar is needed to finish the row. When it is time to learn $6 + 4 = 10$, the student already understands the reality that the fact describes.

LESSON 4

Addition: Symbols, +0
Word Problem Tips

There is an interactive math facts practice page available online at mathusee.com/ drillsheet.html.

As we begin addition and review place value, employ as many senses as possible. That is why we build first. Use the blocks! Even though the picture is sufficient in this case, the more you use the blocks, the better will be the student's understanding. Colour the worksheets to make the connection from the blocks to the picture. Then match with the correct answer on the right. After all this, write the correct numbers on the lines below the picture. Once the problem has been solved, read the equation out loud. See the examples for how to do a problem while building, writing, and saying.

As a readiness exercise, practice counting up by ones from zero to nine and backwards from nine to zero. This is preparing for the one facts and the nine facts. Have the student build the steps with the unit bars as shown in figure 1.

Figure 1

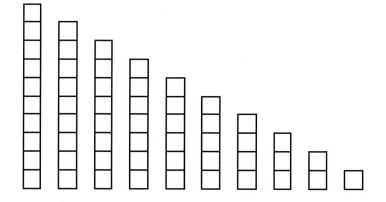

Students understand the concept of "nothing." When teaching 2 + 0, illustrate by saying something like, "We have two dogs, and we didn't get any more today. So we have two plus no more, or 2 + 0 = 2."

Example 1

Solve 2 + 0 =

Place a second two bar and "nothing" above the first two bar.

Build.

2 + 0 = 2   2 + 0 = 2   Write.

"Two plus zero is the same length as two."   Say.

Example 2

Solve 0 + 3 =

Place a second three bar and "nothing" above the first three bar.

Build.

0 + 3 = 3

0 + 3 = 3   Write.

"Zero plus three is the same length as three."   Say.

We will be reinforcing the concept of the *commutative property* of addition in later lessons, but we mention it here because the chart is being introduced for the first time. Notice that there are 100 addition facts to be learned. When you learn 0 + 2, you are also learning 2 + 0. This is encouraging. You can use the examples to illustrate the commutative property without defining it yet. This is not as visual as adding by one or two, so if you want to wait until a later lesson to mention this concept, feel free to do so. The facts that are studied in each lesson will be shaded as we progress. When a student has mastered those facts, have him circle, underline, or colour the same facts on his own sheet (after lesson 4 in the student text).

0 + 0	0 + 1	0 + 2	0 + 3	0 + 4	0 + 5	0 + 6	0 + 7	0 + 8	0 + 9
1 + 0	1 + 1	1 + 2	1 + 3	1 + 4	1 + 5	1 + 6	1 + 7	1 + 8	1 + 9
2 + 0	2 + 1	2 + 2	2 + 3	2 + 4	2 + 5	2 + 6	2 + 7	2 + 8	2 + 9
3 + 0	3 + 1	3 + 2	3 + 3	3 + 4	3 + 5	3 + 6	3 + 7	3 + 8	3 + 9
4 + 0	4 + 1	4 + 2	4 + 3	4 + 4	4 + 5	4 + 6	4 + 7	4 + 8	4 + 9
5 + 0	5 + 1	5 + 2	5 + 3	5 + 4	5 + 5	5 + 6	5 + 7	5 + 8	5 + 9
6 + 0	6 + 1	6 + 2	6 + 3	6 + 4	6 + 5	6 + 6	6 + 7	6 + 8	6 + 9
7 + 0	7 + 1	7 + 2	7 + 3	7 + 4	7 + 5	7 + 6	7 + 7	7 + 8	7 + 9
8 + 0	8 + 1	8 + 2	8 + 3	8 + 4	8 + 5	8 + 6	8 + 7	8 + 8	8 + 9
9 + 0	9 + 1	9 + 2	9 + 3	9 + 4	9 + 5	9 + 6	9 + 7	9 + 8	9 + 9

Word problems begin in this lesson. Read them to the student if necessary. You may use the blocks to illustrate the problems. On the next page are some general tips for teaching word problems.

WORD PROBLEM TIPS

It is often challenging to teach children how to solve word problems. Here are some suggestions for helping your student learn this important skill.

The first step is to realize that word problems require both reading and math comprehension. Don't expect a child to be able to solve a word problem if he does not thoroughly understand the math concepts involved. On the other hand, a student may have a math skill level that is stronger than his or her reading comprehension skills. Below are a number of strategies to improve comprehension skills in the context of story problems. You may decide which ones work best for you and your child.

Strategies for word problems:

1. Ignore numbers at first and read the story. It may help some students to read the question aloud. Every word problem tells a story. Before deciding what math operation is required, let the student retell the story in his own words. Who is involved? Are they receiving gifts, losing something, or dividing a treat?

2. Relate the story to real life, perhaps by using names of family members. For some students, this makes the problem more interesting and relevant.

3. Build, draw, or act out the story. Use the blocks or actual objects when practical. Especially in the lower levels, you may require the student to use the blocks for word problems even when the facts have been learned. Don't be afraid to use a little drama as well. The purpose is to make it as real and meaningful as possible.

4. Look for the common language used in a particular kind of problem. Pay close attention to the word problems on the lesson practice pages, as they model different kinds of language that may be used for the new concept just studied. For example, "altogether" indicates addition. These key words can be useful clues but should not be a substitute for understanding.

5. Look for practical applications that use the concept and ask questions in that context.

6. Have the student invent word problems to illustrate their number problems from the lesson.

Cautions:

1. Unneeded information may be included in the problem. For example, we may be told that Suzie is eight years old, but the eight is irrelevant when adding up the number of gifts she received.

2. Some problems may require more than one step to solve. Model these questions carefully.

3. There may be more than one way to solve some problems. Experience will help the student choose the easier or preferred method.

4. Estimation is a valuable tool for checking an answer. If an answer is unreasonable, it is possible that the wrong method was used to solve the problem.

Addition Facts Sheet

0+0	0+1	0+2	0+3	0+4	0+5	0+6	0+7	0+8	0+9
1+0	1+1	1+2	1+3	1+4	1+5	1+6	1+7	1+8	1+9
2+0	2+1	2+2	2+3	2+4	2+5	2+6	2+7	2+8	2+9
3+0	3+1	3+2	3+3	3+4	3+5	3+6	3+7	3+8	3+9
4+0	4+1	4+2	4+3	4+4	4+5	4+6	4+7	4+8	4+9
5+0	5+1	5+2	5+3	5+4	5+5	5+6	5+7	5+8	5+9
6+0	6+1	6+2	6+3	6+4	6+5	6+6	6+7	6+8	6+9
7+0	7+1	7+2	7+3	7+4	7+5	7+6	7+7	7+8	7+9
8+0	8+1	8+2	8+3	8+4	8+5	8+6	8+7	8+8	8+9
9+0	9+1	9+2	9+3	9+4	9+5	9+6	9+7	9+8	9+9

LESSON 5

Addition: +1, Commutative Property

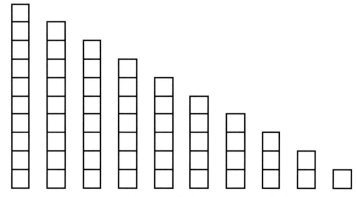

Here is a narrative to use and adapt until the concept of adding one is learned.

Have the student put his/her finger on the three bar. Say, "Point to the number that is one more than that." The student should point to four and say four. Continue to ask questions: "What is one larger than that? . . . If you add one to five, what do you have? . . . What is one greater than six? . . . If I add one to seven what do I have? . . . What is one more than eight?"

Keep going until the student knows "one more than." Change your vocabulary to teach these important words that indicate addition.

When showing the one facts, begin by taking the green one (unit) bar and placing it end to end with the pink three bar. Ask the student if he can find another bar that is the same length as the one bar and the three bar "smooshed" together. This is addition—placing one bar end to end with another bar and finding a third bar that is the same length, in this case the yellow four bar. Now write 1 + 3 = 4 next to the bars while saying, "One plus three is the same length as four," or "One plus three equals four."

The child sees it, builds it, writes it, reads it, and hears it. After this barrage, hopefully he remembers it and understand it!

Example 1

Solve 3 + 1 =

Place the three and the one above the four.

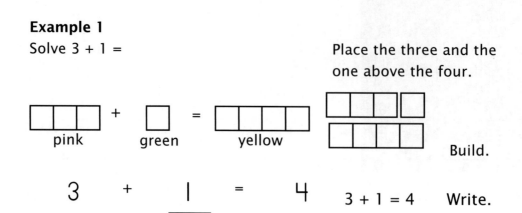

Build.

3 + 1 = 4   Write.

"Three plus one is the same length as, or equal to, four."   Say.

Now that we are using two blocks and "smooshing" them together to make a third number, introduce the commutative property of addition. When enunciating this word, relate it to a worker who commutes to work. If it is 12 kilometres to work one way, then it is 12 kilometres back home. Either way you are travelling, you are still going 12 kilometres.

The *commutative property* means that we can change the order of a problem without changing the answer. In other words, 1 + 5 is the same as 5 + 1. This is an abstract concept that students have to see to understand. An adult that functions well in the abstract has no problem with this, but students generally look at 1 + 5 and 5 + 1 as two different math facts.

You can also show addition vertically as in example 2.

Example 2

Solve $\begin{array}{r} 1 \\ + \ 5 \\ \hline \end{array}$.

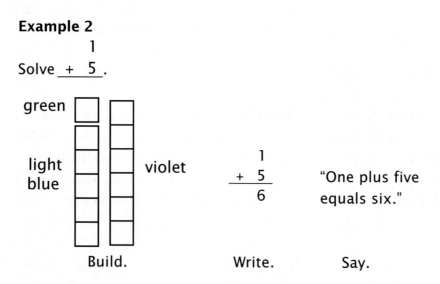

Build.   Write.   Say.

Once you have taught the commutative property, show what a wonderful thing it is: every time we learn one math fact, we are really learning two on the chart. Having memorized the zero and one facts, we have learned 36 out of 100 facts. That is a good start!

0 + 0	0 + 1	0 + 2	0 + 3	0 + 4	0 + 5	0 + 6	0 + 7	0 + 8	0 + 9
1 + 0	1 + 1	1 + 2	1 + 3	1 + 4	1 + 5	1 + 6	1 + 7	1 + 8	1 + 9
2 + 0	2 + 1	2 + 2	2 + 3	2 + 4	2 + 5	2 + 6	2 + 7	2 + 8	2 + 9
3 + 0	3 + 1	3 + 2	3 + 3	3 + 4	3 + 5	3 + 6	3 + 7	3 + 8	3 + 9
4 + 0	4 + 1	4 + 2	4 + 3	4 + 4	4 + 5	4 + 6	4 + 7	4 + 8	4 + 9
5 + 0	5 + 1	5 + 2	5 + 3	5 + 4	5 + 5	5 + 6	5 + 7	5 + 8	5 + 9
6 + 0	6 + 1	6 + 2	6 + 3	6 + 4	6 + 5	6 + 6	6 + 7	6 + 8	6 + 9
7 + 0	7 + 1	7 + 2	7 + 3	7 + 4	7 + 5	7 + 6	7 + 7	7 + 8	7 + 9
8 + 0	8 + 1	8 + 2	8 + 3	8 + 4	8 + 5	8 + 6	8 + 7	8 + 8	8 + 9
9 + 0	9 + 1	9 + 2	9 + 3	9 + 4	9 + 5	9 + 6	9 + 7	9 + 8	9 + 9

Teaching Tip

Using a dry erase board can be helpful for students who have difficulty with fine motor skills. After you have practiced with the blocks, have the student work problems from the lesson on the board. This can also be helpful for students who need a chance to move around while learning. Take this one step further by going outside and using sidewalk chalk!

LESSON 6

Counting to 100; Skip Counting by 10

Since the teens are the most difficult, once the student can count to 20, the progression to counting to 100 should happen naturally. As you progress, "two-ty" is twenty, "three-ty" is thirty, "four-ty" is forty, "five-ty" is fifty, and from that point there is no need to differentiate between the nickname and the proper (or place value) name. Sixty, seventy, eighty, and ninety are all consistent with the pattern of saying the unit name and adding the suffix -ty for ten.

Have the student practice filling in the numbers on the blank lines on the sheets in the student text. You do not need to require this often, just enough for the student to demonstrate the ability to do so.

SKIP COUNTING BY 10

There are several reasons for teaching skip counting. I will mention one reason now, and then more in a later lesson.

Skip counting teaches the concept of multiplication, which is fast adding of the same number. In learning the tens, we are able to fast count groups of ten. Notice how it reinforces writing to 100. The numbers in the far left column of the hundred chart are the multiples of 10: 10, 20, 30 . . .

A good way to practice skip counting is to read the numbers softly from zero to nine, and then have the student shout "10!" Continue counting softly—11, 12, 13 . . . 18, 19—and have the student holler "20!" and so on until the student can skip count from 10 to 100.

Some practical examples of counting by 10 are fingers on both hands, toes on both feet, and pennies in a dime. Notice that the multiples of 10—20, 30, 40, etc.—all end in -ty. The suffix -ty represents ten. So six-ty means six tens, and seven-ty means seven tens.

Example 1

Skip count and write the number on the line. Say it out loud as you count and write. Then write the numbers in the spaces provided beneath the figure.

									10
									20
									30
									40
									50
									60

_____, _____, 30 , 40 , _____, _____

Example 2

Fill in the missing information on the lines.

_____, _____, _____, 40, _____, _____, 70, 80, 90, _____

Solution

10 , 20 , 30 , 40, 50 , 60 , 70, 80, 90, 100

LESSON 7

Addition: +2
Place Value

Before you begin teaching the two facts, practice counting up by twos to ten: 0-2-4-6-8-10. Use the blocks arranged like steps as we did with counting by ones. These are the **even numbers**. Then practice the same skill beginning with one: 1-3-5-7-9. This group of numbers are the **odd numbers**. Going up by two reinforces the two facts. See the game for pre-addition of twos.

Example 1
Solve 5 + 2 =

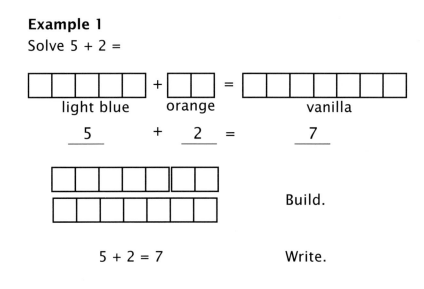

Five plus two is equal to seven.   Say.

Game for Pre-Addition of Twos
   Bigger – Get out the one through nine blocks and stack them in ascending order so that the green unit is on the right. Directly to the left of the unit is the orange two bar, then the pink three bar, and on up to the nine bar. This is identical

to figure 1 in lesson 4. Have the child touch the yellow four bar, then ask the question, "Which number is a two bigger than four?" Then have them touch, or point to, the violet six bar and say "six." Do this for all the unit bars. Interchange the comparative terms such as "more" and "larger" and "bigger." When they've mastered this, simply ask which number is two more than each unit bar.

Example 2

Solve
$$\begin{array}{r} 2 \\ +\ \ 4 \\ \hline \end{array}$$.

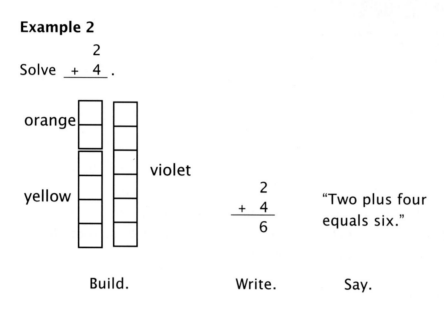

$$\begin{array}{r} 2 \\ +\ \ 4 \\ \hline 6 \end{array}$$

"Two plus four equals six."

Build.   Write.   Say.

In the addition problem in example 1, the numbers 5 and 2 are referred to as the *addends*, and 7 is the *sum*. In example 2, the numbers 2 and 4 are the addends, and the answer 6 is the sum. We add the two addends to form the sum in an addition problem. These terms won't be used a lot, but they are helpful in some instances. For example, the commutative property states that we can change the order of the addends without affecting the sum.

PLACE VALUE

To keep our place value skills fresh and teach a foundational concept of mathematics, we are going to add tens and hundreds. When teaching adding and subtracting, as well as comparing (less than or greater than), I often say, "To compare or combine you must be the same kind." Numbers to be added must have the same place value. When subtracting, the numbers must be the same kind as well. You can't add apples to oranges. You can only add apples to apples and oranges to oranges. So far our adding has been units to units. In example 2 we read two units plus four units is the same as six units. In example 3 we can show that one hundred plus one hundred is two hundreds.

Example 3

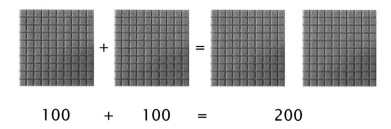

$$100 \quad + \quad 100 \quad = \quad 200$$

In example 4 we see four tens plus two tens is the same as six tens.

Example 4

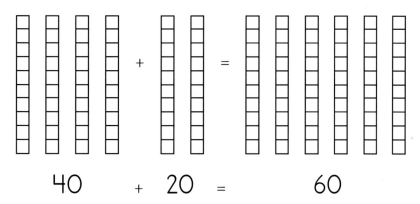

$$40 \quad + \quad 20 \quad = \quad 60$$

Using the commutative property, we can see that after learning the two facts, we have learned 51 out of 100 facts. That is over half!

0+0	0+1	0+2	0+3	0+4	0+5	0+6	0+7	0+8	0+9
1+0	1+1	1+2	1+3	1+4	1+5	1+6	1+7	1+8	1+9
2+0	2+1	2+2	2+3	2+4	2+5	2+6	2+7	2+8	2+9
3+0	3+1	3+2	3+3	3+4	3+5	3+6	3+7	3+8	3+9
4+0	4+1	4+2	4+3	4+4	4+5	4+6	4+7	4+8	4+9
5+0	5+1	5+2	5+3	5+4	5+5	5+6	5+7	5+8	5+9
6+0	6+1	6+2	6+3	6+4	6+5	6+6	6+7	6+8	6+9
7+0	7+1	7+2	7+3	7+4	7+5	7+6	7+7	7+8	7+9
8+0	8+1	8+2	8+3	8+4	8+5	8+6	8+7	8+8	8+9
9+0	9+1	9+2	9+3	9+4	9+5	9+6	9+7	9+8	9+9

We will be reviewing addition and subtraction facts throughout the student textbook. If you find that you need more review of these facts, consult the Math-U-See website, which provides online drill and downloadable worksheets. Visit us online at *mathusee.ca* and look under "**E-Sources.**"

Teaching Tip

Some students respond well to timed practice and any kind of competition. Others find timed drills very intimidating. Be sure to adapt the drills to fit your student. For a non-threatening way to practice, try having the student quiz Mom or Dad on the math facts. After filling in a practice page and making sure the answers are correct, the student reads the problem to a parent. If the parent seems confused or answers incorrectly, the child can correct him from the worksheet. Teaching is a powerful way of learning, so put this to work for your child!

LESSON 8

Solve for Unknown

While teaching addition facts, I like to solve for an unknown for three very important reasons.

1. It reinforces the basic facts.
2. It provides a foundation for subtraction.
3. It familiarizes the students with algebra.

Let's do some examples. Notice that we are not teaching algebra abstractly (just letters and numbers on paper), but concretely with the manipulatives, to give meaning to the letters and numbers. **When solving for the unknown, allow the student to use the blocks for as long as they are needed.**

Example 1

$$\underline{?} + 2 = 9$$

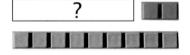

$$\underline{7} + 2 = 9$$

1. Say: "What number plus two is the same as nine?"
2. Build: Put the two above the nine and find the missing piece.
3. Write 7 in the space with the question mark.
4. Say: "Seven plus two is the same as nine."

How you verbalize this is essential to understanding the concept. When you are looking for the correct unit bar, don't be afraid to experiment. I usually reach for the four bar or the five bar first and try it. My ego can handle it, and I want to show that it is okay to eliminate possibilities. I like to encourage a student's attempts to experiment to find the correct solution. Later we can move to writing X + 2 = 9. In this case we are using a letter because we don't know exactly what number makes this the same, or equal, or an equation. I define algebra as, "When we don't know what number to use, pick a letter!"

Now, although we are happy that the student can solve for an unknown, we are not satisfied until he can make a word problem out of this equation. After all, the end product of our math instruction is to apply it to real-life situations. For our problem you might say that you need nine dollars by the weekend and you have two. How much more do you need? Or, Charlie Brown has two players. How many more does he need for his baseball team (nine players)? As the student works on the worksheets, encourage him to make word problems or story problems to fit the equations. This will help him later when we move in the opposite direction and he is asked to write an equation for the story problem.

Also in this lesson, practice counting from 0 to 100.

Example 2

$\underline{?} + 2 = 5$

1. Say: "What number plus two is the same as five?"
2. Place the two above the five and find the missing piece.
3. Write 3 in the space with the question mark.

$\underline{3} + 2 = 5$

4. Say: "Three plus two is the same as five."

Games for Problem Solving

Who are you? Who am I? – Example: "Together we are seven. You are a one; what am I?" When the student has mastered numbers added up to 10, extend the numbers past 10.

Both Sides the Same – Get a large piece of white paper and draw a line down the middle. Place a number bar on one side and a smaller bar on the other side, with a third piece hidden under a bowl or piece of paper. For example, place a seven bar on one side, and showing on the opposite side is a two bar and a bowl. Ask what is hidden under the bowl and say, "What plus two is the same as seven?" When they figure it out, pick up the bowl to reveal the five bar. Start with smaller numbers and place progressively larger amounts on the known side.

LESSON 9

Addition: +9, Mental Math

In this lesson we are adding by nines. The idea of making or wanting to be ten will be your fun-dation for regrouping. First practice counting backwards by one using the game at the end of this lesson. Taking one away, or counting down by one, is essential to our approach to learning to add by nine.

I like to introduce this with a short narrative about how nine isn't content because he wants to be ten. Ask most nine-year-olds how old they want to be, and they say, "Ten!" Children understand Mr. Nine. Next ask, "What does nine need to have added to him to be ten?" "One unit!" Nine is therefore always on the prowl, looking for one more so he can be ten! Using a nine bar and several green unit bars, let's create the equation 9 + 5. Ham it up any way you can, perhaps having the student look away or close his eyes. In that instant nine takes one to be ten (or "onety").

Example 1
Solve 9 + 5 =

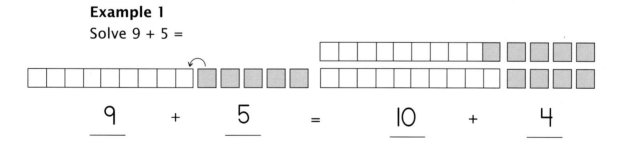

$$9 \quad + \quad 5 \quad = \quad 10 \quad + \quad 4$$

Nine plus five is equal to ten plus four, or fourteen.

Note: This will be the first time a student has added ten to a number. Simply apply what the student knows about place value. Start with ten and ask what you would have if you added two more: for example: 10 + 2 = 12. Put together a ten bar and a two bar to illustrate this.

In example 1, we still have one nine and five units, and they are the same length as one ten and four units. Nine is finally happy, and 10 + 4 is 14 ("onety-four"). We can also see that 9 + 5 = 14. The original five has been decreased by one from five to four. And nine has been increased by one to be ten. This is what regrouping or carrying is all about!

To remember the written code, let's make the circle on the top of the numeral 9 the end of a vacuum nozzle. Nine is always "sucking up" one. Making the noise is fun and multi-sensory. When a child sees 9, he thinks "one less" and sucks up one or makes whatever noise you make. Practice the nines now until the student understands and feels confident adding by nine. Be sure to practice "taking one away" first with the game on the next page.

There are addition facts songs on the CD *Skip Counting and Addition Facts Songs*. These are designed to assist the student in memorizing his facts.

Another way to solve adding by nine is to use the coloured unit bars. For 9 + 5 pick out the lime green bar and the light blue five bar. Place them end to end and say, "Nine plus five is the same as ten plus what?" Have the student find the yellow four bar and place it at the end of the blue ten bar. Then say, "Nine plus five is the same as ten plus four, or fourteen." See example 2. Choose whichever way helps the student understand the concept most effectively. Don't forget to use the same strategies as in previous lessons of presenting the problems by building, writing, and saying to assist in memorizing and understanding these facts.

Example 2
Solve 9 + 5 =

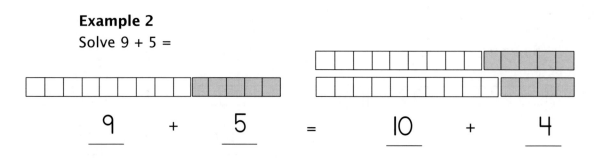

Nine plus five is equal to ten plus four, or fourteen.

With this lesson, we have learned 64 out of 100 facts. That is over half!

0 + 0	0 + 1	0 + 2	0 + 3	0 + 4	0 + 5	0 + 6	0 + 7	0 + 8	0 + 9
1 + 0	1 + 1	1 + 2	1 + 3	1 + 4	1 + 5	1 + 6	1 + 7	1 + 8	1 + 9
2 + 0	2 + 1	2 + 2	2 + 3	2 + 4	2 + 5	2 + 6	2 + 7	2 + 8	2 + 9
3 + 0	3 + 1	3 + 2	3 + 3	3 + 4	3 + 5	3 + 6	3 + 7	3 + 8	3 + 9
4 + 0	4 + 1	4 + 2	4 + 3	4 + 4	4 + 5	4 + 6	4 + 7	4 + 8	4 + 9
5 + 0	5 + 1	5 + 2	5 + 3	5 + 4	5 + 5	5 + 6	5 + 7	5 + 8	5 + 9
6 + 0	6 + 1	6 + 2	6 + 3	6 + 4	6 + 5	6 + 6	6 + 7	6 + 8	6 + 9
7 + 0	7 + 1	7 + 2	7 + 3	7 + 4	7 + 5	7 + 6	7 + 7	7 + 8	7 + 9
8 + 0	8 + 1	8 + 2	8 + 3	8 + 4	8 + 5	8 + 6	8 + 7	8 + 8	8 + 9
9 + 0	9 + 1	9 + 2	9 + 3	9 + 4	9 + 5	9 + 6	9 + 7	9 + 8	9 + 9

Game to Precede Adding by 9

Smaller – Get out the one through nine blocks and stack them in ascending order so the green unit is on the right. Ask the question, "Which number is a one smaller than ( )?" or "Which number is a one less than ( )?" Do this until the student knows each one; only then move to learning the nine facts.

MENTAL MATH

Mental math problems can be used to keep the facts alive in the memory and to develop mental math skills. The teacher should say the problem slowly enough so that the student comprehends it, and then walk him through increasingly difficult exercises. The purpose is to stretch but not discourage. You decide where that line is! See the example below, along with some suggested problems to try.

Example 3
2 + 3 + 1 = ?   "Two plus three plus one equals what number?"

The student thinks, "2 + 3 = 5, and 5 + 1 = 6." At first you will need to go slowly enough for him or her to verbalize the intermediate step. As skills increase, the student should be able to just give the answer.

Starting with this lesson, every third lesson in this instruction manual will have some suggested mental math problems for you to read aloud to your student. Try a few at a time, and remember to go quite slowly at first.

1. Four plus one plus one equals what number? (6)

2. Two plus two plus zero equals what number? (4)

3. Five plus one plus two equals what number? (8)

4. Three plus two plus two equals what number? (7)

5. Eight plus one plus five equals what number? (14)

6. One plus three plus zero equals what number? (4)

7. Six plus two plus one equals what number? (9)

8. Five plus two plus two equals what number? (9)

9. Seven plus two plus eight equals what number? (17)

10. Nine plus zero plus one equals what number? (10)

LESSON 10

Addition: +8

The "solve for the unknown" problems on the systematic review pages introduce the use of X for the unknown. When we don't know what number to use, we use a letter (any letter may be used). This is a simple but accurate definition of algebra. Write the correct answer over or under the letter. We don't need to write X = 3 at this point.

Before you begin addition by eight, practice counting backwards by twos. Have the student be able to say 8-6-4-2-0 and 9-7-5-3-1 before going any further. See the game near the end of this lesson.

Remember how we added nines? Now we are going to vacuum two! This is adding by eight. Eight has two circles in the number or two vacuum nozzles. Mr. Eight wants to be ten just like Mr. Nine. When we add eight to any number, we take two from that number and add a ten. In example 1, take the brown eight bar and then place five green unit bars beside it. Then make the vacuum noise and take two of the green unit pieces and place them next to eight, making ten. Then put a ten bar on top of or beside the 8 + 2. The student should see that 8 + 5 is the same as 10 + 3, or 13.

Example 1
Solve 8 + 5 =

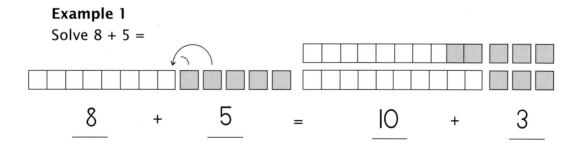

Eight plus five is equal to ten plus three, or thirteen.

We can solve adding by eight another way using the coloured unit bars.

Example 2
Solve 8 + 5 =

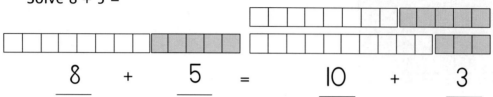

$$\underline{8} \quad + \quad \underline{5} \quad = \quad \underline{10} \quad + \quad \underline{3}$$

Eight plus five is equal to ten plus three, or thirteen.

Example 3
Solve 8 + 7 =

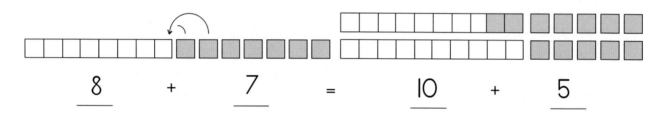

$$\underline{8} \quad + \quad \underline{7} \quad = \quad \underline{10} \quad + \quad \underline{5}$$

Eight plus seven is equal to ten plus five, or fifteen.

Example 4
Solve 8 + 7 =

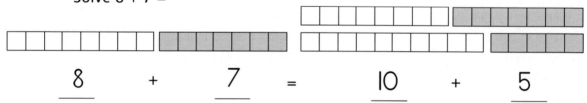

$$\underline{8} \quad + \quad \underline{7} \quad = \quad \underline{10} \quad + \quad \underline{5}$$

Eight plus seven is equal to ten plus five, or fifteen.

With the eight facts mastered, we now know 75 out of 100 facts. Good job! There are only 25 more to go.

0 + 0	0 + 1	0 + 2	0 + 3	0 + 4	0 + 5	0 + 6	0 + 7	0 + 8	0 + 9
1 + 0	1 + 1	1 + 2	1 + 3	1 + 4	1 + 5	1 + 6	1 + 7	1 + 8	1 + 9
2 + 0	2 + 1	2 + 2	2 + 3	2 + 4	2 + 5	2 + 6	2 + 7	2 + 8	2 + 9
3 + 0	3 + 1	3 + 2	3 + 3	3 + 4	3 + 5	3 + 6	3 + 7	3 + 8	3 + 9
4 + 0	4 + 1	4 + 2	4 + 3	4 + 4	4 + 5	4 + 6	4 + 7	4 + 8	4 + 9
5 + 0	5 + 1	5 + 2	5 + 3	5 + 4	5 + 5	5 + 6	5 + 7	5 + 8	5 + 9
6 + 0	6 + 1	6 + 2	6 + 3	6 + 4	6 + 5	6 + 6	6 + 7	6 + 8	6 + 9
7 + 0	7 + 1	7 + 2	7 + 3	7 + 4	7 + 5	7 + 6	7 + 7	7 + 8	7 + 9
8 + 0	8 + 1	8 + 2	8 + 3	8 + 4	8 + 5	8 + 6	8 + 7	8 + 8	8 + 9
9 + 0	9 + 1	9 + 2	9 + 3	9 + 4	9 + 5	9 + 6	9 + 7	9 + 8	9 + 9

Game to Precede Adding by 8

Smaller – Get out the one through nine blocks and stack them in ascending order so the green unit is on the right. Ask the question, "Which number is a two smaller than ( )?" or "Which number is a two less than ( )?" Do this until they know each one, and then move to learning the eight facts.

Teaching Tip

Try saying the answer and letting the student give an acceptable problem to match the answer you said. Don't limit the response to facts that you have already studied. This is a good activity to do in the car.

Shapes: Circles and Triangles
Skip Counting by 2

A *circle* is a line drawn around a point. Every spot on the circle is the same distance from the centre. You can draw a circle with a compass. The distance between the point of the compass and the pencil is the same as the distance from the centre (the compass point) and the circle (drawn by the pencil). Another way to draw a circle is to get a piece of string and tie one end to a nail and the other end to a pencil. Hold the nail, or nail it into a board. Then, keeping the string taut, draw a circle with the pencil.

Look around you and write down examples of circles. Here are a few ideas to help prime the pump: plates, bottoms of glasses and bottles, coins, clock faces, door knobs, ceiling lights, and tires.

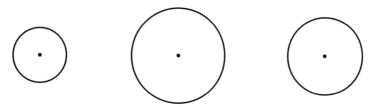

A *triangle* has three sides. The prefix *tri-* represents three as in tricycle, which has three wheels, or tripod, which has three legs. Observe other examples of triangles in your environment.

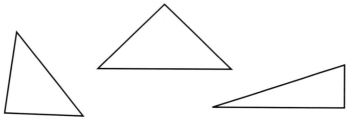

SKIP COUNTING BY 2

For those of you who have completed the *Primer* curriculum, this will be review. Skip counting is a good foundation for many skills to be learned in the future.

Skip counting is the ability to count groups of the same number quickly. For example, if you were to skip count by threes you would skip the one and the two and say "three," then skip the four and the five and say "six," then "9-12-15-18," etc. Skip counting by sevens is 7-14-21-28-35-42-49-56-63-70.

There are four reasons for teaching skip counting.

1. It lays a solid foundation for learning the multiplication facts. 3 + 3 + 3 + 3 may be written as 3 x 4. If a child can skip count, he can say 3-6-9-12. Then he could read 3 x 4 as "3 counted 4 times is 12." As you learn your skip-counting facts, you are learning all your multiplication facts in order.

2. Skip counting teaches the concept of multiplication. I had a teacher tell me that her students had successfully memorized their facts but didn't know what they had acquired. After she taught them the skip-counting facts, they understood what they had learned. Multiplication is fast adding of the same number.

3. It is helpful as a skill in itself. Skip counting is counting in multiples of a certain number. A pharmacist attending a workshop told me he skip counted pills as he put them into bottles.

4. It teaches you the multiples of a number that are so important when making equivalent fractions and finding common denominators. 2/5 = 4/10 = 6/15 = 8/20. The numbers 2-4-6-8 are the multiples of two and 5-10-15-20 are the multiples of five.

In this lesson we will be counting by twos. When introducing this, try pointing to each square. (See examples on the next page.) As you count the squares, say the first number quietly and then ask the student to say the second number more loudly. (One happy customer in Florida asks his child to use his "inside voice" to verbalize the first number and his "outside voice" to say the second number. Another father with a military background has his son stand at attention and bark the skip count facts loudly in cadence!) Continue this practice, doing it more quietly each time until you are silently pointing to the first block, while they say the number loudly as you point to the second square. On the practice sheets, write numbers only in the squares with lines in them. See examples 1 and 2. In example 3, we are counting geometric shapes in groups of two.

Some other practical examples of counting by twos are counting eyes, ears, hands, feet, shoes, and socks. You might ask the student to count all the eyes or shoes in the family or in the classroom. This is also a good time to learn common prefixes like *bi-*, which denotes two, as in bicycle or biped.

Another way to teach this skill is with the *Skip Count and Addition Song Book*. Included is a CD with the skip count songs from the twos to the nines sung to popular tunes taken from hymns and Christmas carols.

Special Note to Teachers

In the *Alpha* curriculum we are going to learn to skip count by 2, 5, and 10. The rest of the skip count facts will be learned in *Gamma*. If you think that your student(s) are ready to learn all of the skip counting facts now, feel free to have them do so. The skip count songs enable children to learn these facts quickly. Have fun with the songs and facts.

Example 1
How many boxes are there?

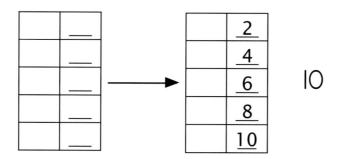

Example 2
How many boxes are there?

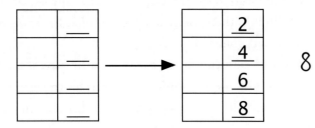

8

Example 3
How many triangles are there?

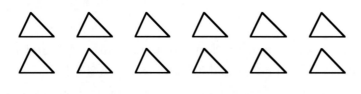

2-4-6-8-10-12   12 triangles

LESSON 12

Addition: Doubles

The next step in our adding is to learn the doubles: 3 + 3, 4 + 4, 5 + 5, 6 + 6, and 7 + 7. Most children know these facts, except for 7 + 7. Here is 7 + 7 = 14 shown with the blocks.

Example 1
Solve 7 + 7 =

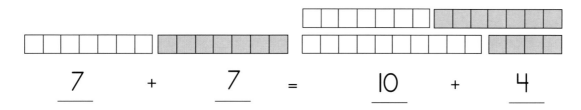

$$\underline{7} \quad + \quad \underline{7} \quad = \quad \underline{10} \quad + \quad \underline{4}$$

Seven plus seven is equal to ten plus four, or fourteen.

Example 2
Solve 6 + 6 =

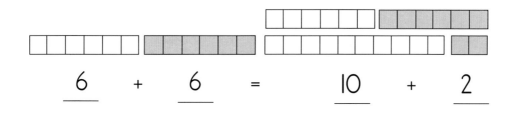

$$\underline{6} \quad + \quad \underline{6} \quad = \quad \underline{10} \quad + \quad \underline{2}$$

Six plus six is equal to ten plus two, or twelve.

Example 3
Solve 5 + 5 =

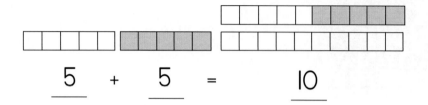

$$\underline{5} + \underline{5} = \underline{10}$$

Five plus five is equal to ten.

At this stage younger children may or may not know how to read. As the teacher, use your discretion about how much to emphasize recognizing number words. Here are the numbers from zero to ten. On the student worksheets the words will be provided so the student can select the appropriate answer.

0 - zero	4 - four	8 - eight
1 - one	5 - five	9 - nine
2 - two	6 - six	10 - ten
3 - three	7 - seven	

Example 4
four plus two equals _____

$$\underline{4} + \underline{2} = \underline{}$$

Solution
four plus two equals s̈ix

$$\underline{4} + \underline{2} = \underline{6}$$

With the addition of the doubles, we have finished memorizing 80 out of 100 facts. With only 20 facts left, you are to be congratulated.

0+0	0+1	0+2	0+3	0+4	0+5	0+6	0+7	0+8	0+9
1+0	1+1	1+2	1+3	1+4	1+5	1+6	1+7	1+8	1+9
2+0	2+1	2+2	2+3	2+4	2+5	2+6	2+7	2+8	2+9
3+0	3+1	3+2	3+3	3+4	3+5	3+6	3+7	3+8	3+9
4+0	4+1	4+2	4+3	4+4	4+5	4+6	4+7	4+8	4+9
5+0	5+1	5+2	5+3	5+4	5+5	5+6	5+7	5+8	5+9
6+0	6+1	6+2	6+3	6+4	6+5	6+6	6+7	6+8	6+9
7+0	7+1	7+2	7+3	7+4	7+5	7+6	7+7	7+8	7+9
8+0	8+1	8+2	8+3	8+4	8+5	8+6	8+7	8+8	8+9
9+0	9+1	9+2	9+3	9+4	9+5	9+6	9+7	9+8	9+9

Mental Math

Here are some more questions to read to your student.

1. Four plus four plus one equals what number? (9)

2. Two plus three plus five equals what number? (10)

3. One plus six plus two equals what number? (9)

4. Six plus two plus seven equals what number? (15)

5. Zero plus nine plus nine equals what number? (18)

6. One plus two plus three equals what number? (6)

7. Two plus four plus eight equals what number? (14)

8. Eight plus zero plus four equals what number? (12)

9. Three plus three plus nine equals what number? (15)

10. Two plus two plus two equals what number? (6)

ADDITION: DOUBLES - LESSON 12 **63**

Teaching Tip 1

Years ago, when I was tutoring a student who didn't pick up new material with a normal presentation, I developed a new strategy. With most kids I have worked with, once you show them a few examples, they are ready to try one themselves. Watching the video and doing a few examples is what I call a normal presentation of a new concept, but with this particular student that didn't work. What I did was to present the material and then do four or five examples without asking him to participate—just to watch. I would take a problem, build it, write it, and talk through the process as I worked toward the solution. I did this for all the problems. Sometimes I would ask him to select the problems that I should solve. That was all I did for the first day of a new lesson. The second day I would do a few more problems and then ask him to do one or two. By that time he had seen me do at least six problems, and he felt comfortable enough to try one himself.

The reason I came upon this approach was that I noticed two examples were not nearly enough. He needed more time to assimilate a new concept. Because of his inability to grasp the new material in a short amount of time, he would become anxious and stressed and be even less able to understand the topic at hand. When he knew that he would not be required to participate the first day, he was able to relax and learn without becoming nervous about the prospect of having to do a problem after only a few examples.

I also realized how effective correct input and modeling is to learning. Our culture is geared to output and tests and quizzes and scores. By taking the time to present the material clearly and correctly, the input improved dramatically, and the student was able to comprehend better because he knew exactly what was expected. This is definitely a deductive approach. You may have a student who requires more freedom in finding solutions who would benefit from an inductive approach, but my student blossomed with this approach.

This student also had short-term memory issues, so I couldn't spend too many days on the new material, or he would forget what he learned in the previous lesson. So I had to move to the review sheets after just a few days with the new material and intersperse the lesson practice sheets with the systematic review sheets.

Teaching Tip 2

Now that you have learned a few sets of math facts, here is a tip to help students commit them to memory. When we solve for an unknown, one addend and the sum is given, and we have to find the missing addend. In $X + 2 = 7$, we know the 2 and the 7, and we have to find the missing 5. The answer is $5 + 2 = 7$. In solving for the unknown, we are reviewing addition, taking beginning steps in algebra, and laying a foundation for subtraction. In subtraction we will have $7 - 2 = 5$. These are the same numbers, just a different order than $5 + 2 = 7$. These numbers, 2, 5, and 7, can be called a trio. You have already covered adding by 8 and by 9. To cement these facts in your students' memory, you could come at what they have learned from a slightly different angle to help them in using trios. Ask what the missing number in the trio is when given 4 and 13. The answer would be a 9. Explain that this technique is very similar to how we have been solving for an unknown such as $X + 4 = 13$ or $4 + X = 13$. You are simply being asked to find the missing information in a different way.

I hope these tips have been helpful.

Steve Demme

LESSON 13

Rectangles, Squares; Skip Counting by 5

Rectangle means "right angle." *Rect* comes from a German word meaning "right." A *right angle* is a square corner. If you find an object with four square corners, it is a rectangle. Look around you and see how many rectangles there are. This piece of paper is a rectangle. See how many others the student can identify.

Notice that the opposite sides of a rectangle are the same length.

A *square* is a special kind of rectangle. It has four right angles, so it is a rectangle. However, we also notice that all four sides are the same length. A rectangle with all four sides the same length is called a square. Here's another way of thinking of it: A square has four right angles and four sides the same length.

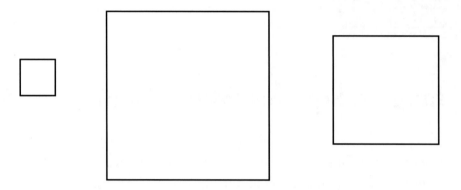

Even though a square is a special kind of rectangle, at this level students should count squares and rectangles as two separate shapes.

SKIP COUNTING BY 5

In this lesson we are reviewing skip counting by fives. Use the same techniques to introduce and teach this important skill that have worked for skip counting by twos and tens. Some practical examples are fingers on one hand, toes on a foot, pennies in a nickel, players on a basketball team, and sides of a pentagon.

Example 1

As with the twos and tens, skip count and write the number on the line. Say it out loud as you count and write. Then write the numbers in the spaces provided beneath the figure.

				5
				10
				15
				20

5, _____, _____, _____

Example 2
Fill in the missing information on the lines.

5, ___, 15, ___, ___, 30, ___, 40, 45, ___

Solution

5, _10_, 15, _20_, _25_, 30, _35_, 40, 45, _50_

Telling Time

Now that your student can skip count by tens and fives, he has the necessary skills to learn how to tell time. Telling time was presented in *Primer* and is taught again in the next book, *Beta*. If you want to review what you learned in *Primer* or introduce telling time now for the first time, consult appendices A and B for instructions on this topic.

Addition: Doubles +1
Associative Property

Once the doubles are mastered, we build on this knowledge with the doubles plus one. If you know 3 + 3 = 6, then you can see that 3 + 4 = 7. In the same way, think 4 + 5 = 4 + 4 + 1 = 9. Got it? Some call these particular facts the neighbours of the doubles. They say that 4 + 5 is the neighbour of 4 + 4 and 5 + 5. If you don't work it out as in the examples, think that 4 + 5 is between 4 + 4, which is 8, and 5 + 5, which is 10. Thus 4 + 5 must be 9. Notice that we are not working by sheer rote memory; we are encouraging thinking and understanding. Both are necessary in learning and remembering math facts.

This is a good place to introduce the *associative property* of addition. Think of associating with two other friends. Only two people can associate at one time. The associative property states that you can regroup (or re-associate) the addends in an addition problem without affecting the sum. In the following example, we break up 4 into 3 + 1. Notice how 3 and 1 associate at first (in 4), and then are regrouped to form 3 and 3 (in 6). The parentheses denote who is associating with whom.

Example 1
Solve 3 + 4 =

3   +   4   =   3   +   3 + 1 =   6   +   1 = 7

3 + 4 = 3 + (3 + 1) = (3 + 3) + 1 = 6 + 1 = 7

Example 2

Solve 5 + 6 =

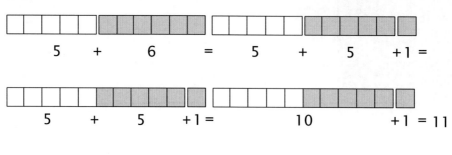

5 + 6 = 5 + (5 + 1) = (5 + 5) + 1 = 10 + 1 = 11

The doubles plus one are found above and below the doubles. There are eight new ones. Now we have accomplished all of the shaded areas on the chart. Eighty out of 100 facts have been learned!

0+0	0+1	0+2	0+3	0+4	0+5	0+6	0+7	0+8	0+9
1+0	1+1	1+2	1+3	1+4	1+5	1+6	1+7	1+8	1+9
2+0	2+1	2+2	2+3	2+4	2+5	2+6	2+7	2+8	2+9
3+0	3+1	3+2	3+3	3+4	3+5	3+6	3+7	3+8	3+9
4+0	4+1	4+2	4+3	4+4	4+5	4+6	4+7	4+8	4+9
5+0	5+1	5+2	5+3	5+4	5+5	5+6	5+7	5+8	5+9
6+0	6+1	6+2	6+3	6+4	6+5	6+6	6+7	6+8	6+9
7+0	7+1	7+2	7+3	7+4	7+5	7+6	7+7	7+8	7+9
8+0	8+1	8+2	8+3	8+4	8+5	8+6	8+7	8+8	8+9
9+0	9+1	9+2	9+3	9+4	9+5	9+6	9+7	9+8	9+9

Teaching Tip

Often a student will have only a few facts that are difficult to remember. Choose one of them at a time and make it the "fact of the day." Post this fact on the refrigerator or some other place where it will be seen often. Then ask the student frequently during the day to tell you the answer. After talking about one fact all day long, you may find the student knows that one best of all.

LESSON 15

Addition: Making 10

There are two ways to teach addition facts. I call the first the logical way, which is used to teach most of the facts. The second is the family method, which we use for the 10 family. Take a 10 bar and place it on the table or floor. Using two of the coloured unit bars, how many ways can you make 10? Be sure you verbally say "two unit bars" because addition facts are the combination of two facts, not three or four facts. In figure 1 you can see five ways of making 10. They are 1 + 9, 2 + 8, 3 + 7, 4 + 6, and 5 + 5. Our 10 family is made up of five different facts. After you build these, write them down and say them to make it multi-sensory.

Figure 1

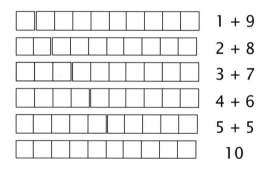

The ten facts and the nine facts (4 + 5, 6 + 3, 7 + 2, 8 + 1) are the most important ones to teach using the family method. Make sure these facts are "down cold." (Making nine is taught in the next lesson.)

Games for Making 10

Build a Wall - See who can build the highest wall that is 10 units long, using two bars in each row, snapped together. After you build your wall, write down the equation that corresponds to the two pieces in that length of wall. If the first floor is a six bar and a four bar, then the equation is $6 + 4 = 10$.

Fill in the Space - Fill in the blank space with the correct bar. In this game you are still building on the 10, but instead of placing two bars to be the same length as 10, you place only one and the student places the other one. Then it is his turn to place one, and you figure out the length of the missing piece. Example: Begin with a 10 bar, and then choose a seven bar and snap it on top of the 10 bar. Have the student find the piece that makes 10, in this case the three bar. Finally, have the student write down $7 + 3 = 10$. Now let him or her be the teacher and choose a different piece, while you find the missing unit bar and write the addition fact.

Race to a Hundred (and Race You Back) - Use either playing cards (face cards removed and aces are ones), or the cards you made for Pick a Card, or a 10-sided die. Draw a card, let's say an eight. Pick up the eight bar and stick it on your 100 square. If your next card is a one or a two, no problem; just stick it by the eight. If it is a seven, put it somewhere else on the 100 square. On your next turn, pick another number and be on the lookout for blocks that can even out a line, such as a two with an eight. Start at zero and accumulate blocks until you reach a 100 and cover the entire 100 square.

"Race You Back" means you don't have to motivate them to put their blocks away! In this game you go in reverse and take off the value of the card. When they get good at this, require each row of 10 to be filled in from top to bottom as they go. This forces dynamic addition/subtraction to be accomplished. By dynamic, I mean that blocks will have to be "traded in" to get the correct blocks that will fill in the required amount. Here's an example: first roll is seven and second roll is six. The six would be broken into two threes; one would fill in the first row with a seven, and the second three would start the next row. For the race back to zero, I let them pull the rolled number from anywhere within the hundred. A little dynamic work will be needed at the "100 point" and back near zero. Go as slowly as necessary. For example, there is only a five to go to be finished, and the student rolls an eight. The eight must be "broken" into a five and a three.

Example 1

Solve 3 + 7 =

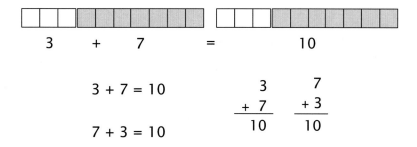

3 + 7 = 10

7 + 3 = 10

$$3 \atop {+ 7 \atop 10}$$ $$7 \atop {+ 3 \atop 10}$$

Example 2

Solve 6 + 4 =

6 + 4 = 10

4 + 6 = 10

$$6 \atop {+ 4 \atop 10}$$ $$4 \atop {+ 6 \atop 10}$$

We have emphasized that addition is to be taught with the different bars so that the student will learn the facts without counting. This lesson would be a good place to reinforce the concept that addition is fast counting. It may seem like a contradiction, but now that they have learned so many of their facts, show them that they can find the answer to 5 + 5 by counting 1-2-3-4-5 and then 6-7-8-9-10. Show them that adding is so much quicker and more efficient. Affirm that learning their facts without counting is far superior to counting, and affirm how well they are doing, while reminding them that adding is fast counting.

The making-10 facts cross the chart diagonally. There are four new ones. We have only eight more facts to go. Good work! Ninety-two out of 100 facts are behind us.

0 + 0	0 + 1	0 + 2	0 + 3	0 + 4	0 + 5	0 + 6	0 + 7	0 + 8	0 + 9
1 + 0	1 + 1	1 + 2	1 + 3	1 + 4	1 + 5	1 + 6	1 + 7	1 + 8	1 + 9
2 + 0	2 + 1	2 + 2	2 + 3	2 + 4	2 + 5	2 + 6	2 + 7	2 + 8	2 + 9
3 + 0	3 + 1	3 + 2	3 + 3	3 + 4	3 + 5	3 + 6	3 + 7	3 + 8	3 + 9
4 + 0	4 + 1	4 + 2	4 + 3	4 + 4	4 + 5	4 + 6	4 + 7	4 + 8	4 + 9
5 + 0	5 + 1	5 + 2	5 + 3	5 + 4	5 + 5	5 + 6	5 + 7	5 + 8	5 + 9
6 + 0	6 + 1	6 + 2	6 + 3	6 + 4	6 + 5	6 + 6	6 + 7	6 + 8	6 + 9
7 + 0	7 + 1	7 + 2	7 + 3	7 + 4	7 + 5	7 + 6	7 + 7	7 + 8	7 + 9
8 + 0	8 + 1	8 + 2	8 + 3	8 + 4	8 + 5	8 + 6	8 + 7	8 + 8	8 + 9
9 + 0	9 + 1	9 + 2	9 + 3	9 + 4	9 + 5	9 + 6	9 + 7	9 + 8	9 + 9

Mental Math

Here are some more questions to read to your student. Don't try the longer problems unless the student is comfortable with the shorter ones.

1. Three plus four, plus three equals what number? (10)

2. Six plus one, plus seven equals what number? (14)

3. One plus eight, plus eight equals what number? (17)

4. Two plus three, plus four equals what number? (9)

5. Nine plus zero, plus three equals what number? (12)

6. One plus one, plus two, plus three equals what number? (7)

7. Two plus one, plus zero, plus seven equals what number? (10)

8. Two plus two, plus one, plus six equals what number? (11)

9. Three plus one, plus four, plus one equals what number? (9)

10. Four plus four, plus one, plus five equals what number? (14)

LESSON 16

Addition: Making 9

Use the same technique for making nine as you did for making ten. Place a nine bar on the bottom and see how many ways you can make nine using two unit bars in each row. You will discover 1 + 8, 2 + 7, 3 + 6, and 5 + 4. The only new one is 3 + 6. We have already learned 1 + 8 in the one facts, 2 + 7 as one of the two facts, and 5 + 4 as a double plus one.

Figure 1

1 + 8
2 + 7
3 + 6
4 + 5
9

Making nine will prove beneficial when learning to multiply. Make sure these facts are thoroughly mastered before proceeding to the next lesson.

Games for Making 9

Build a Wall - Remember playing this game when learning the tens family? Let's adapt it to the nines. See who can build the highest wall nine units long, using two bars in each row snapped onto the previous row. As you build your wall, write down the equation that corresponds to the two pieces in each row or floor. If the first floor is a five bar and a four bar, then write the equation 5 + 4 = 9, and say, "five plus four equals nine."

Fill in the Space - Another game is to fill in the blank space with the correct bar. You are still building on the nine, but instead of placing two bars to be the same length as nine, you place only one and the student places the other one. Then it is his turn to place one, and you figure out the length of the missing piece. Example: Begin with a nine bar, and then choose a seven bar and snap it on top of the nine bar. Have the student find the piece that makes nine, in this case the two bar. Have the student write down 7 + 2 = 9, and say, "seven plus two equals nine." Then let him or her be the teacher and choose a different piece, and you find the missing unit bar and write the addition fact.

Wannabe 9 - Get out the one bar through the nine bar. Set the bars next to each other and ask how much more each needs in order to be a nine, or to "grow up to be a big nine."

Example 1

Solve 3 + 6 =

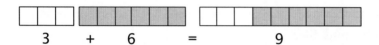

$$3 + 6 = 9$$

$$\begin{array}{r} 3 \\ + 6 \\ \hline 9 \end{array}$$

Example 2

Solve 6 + 3 =

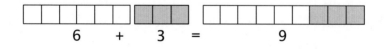

$$6 + 3 = 9$$

$$\begin{array}{r} 6 \\ + 3 \\ \hline 9 \end{array}$$

The making-nine facts are found diagonally above making ten. There are only two new ones. With only six facts to go, we can see the finish line. Don't give up now—you are almost done! Ninety-four out of 100 facts have been learned.

0+0	0+1	0+2	0+3	0+4	0+5	0+6	0+7	0+8	0+9
1+0	1+1	1+2	1+3	1+4	1+5	1+6	1+7	1+8	1+9
2+0	2+1	2+2	2+3	2+4	2+5	2+6	2+7	2+8	2+9
3+0	3+1	3+2	3+3	3+4	3+5	3+6	3+7	3+8	3+9
4+0	4+1	4+2	4+3	4+4	4+5	4+6	4+7	4+8	4+9
5+0	5+1	5+2	5+3	5+4	5+5	5+6	5+7	5+8	5+9
6+0	6+1	6+2	6+3	6+4	6+5	6+6	6+7	6+8	6+9
7+0	7+1	7+2	7+3	7+4	7+5	7+6	7+7	7+8	7+9
8+0	8+1	8+2	8+3	8+4	8+5	8+6	8+7	8+8	8+9
9+0	9+1	9+2	9+3	9+4	9+5	9+6	9+7	9+8	9+9

Teaching Tip

The online drill program at mathusee.com can be set to drill any combination of previously learned facts that you wish. When you need a fresh approach to learning the facts, try inventing your own games using cards or dominoes.

LESSON 17

Addition of the Extras: 3 + 5, 4 + 7, 5 + 7

The extras don't fit into a pattern like the eights or nines do, neither are they a part of the 9 or 10 families of math facts. They are also the last three facts to be learned. Actually, there are six facts counting their commutative counterparts. Take your time and finish up the task of learning all of the addition facts.

Adding 3 + 5, 4 + 7, and 5 + 7 provides a good opportunity to use what the student has learned to figure out the new material. Looking at 4 + 7, they might say, "Well, that is one more than 3 + 7, which is 10, so the answer must be 11!" Looking at 3 + 5 they might say, "Well, that is one less than 3 + 6, which is 9, so the answer must be 8!" Give them a chance to figure out alternative means, and encourage them to discover their own formulas and patterns. There are several ways to arrive at each answer.

Example 1
Solve 3 + 5 =

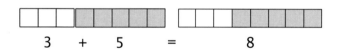

$$3 + 5 = 8$$

$$5 + 3 = 8$$

$$\begin{array}{r} 3 \\ + 5 \\ \hline 8 \end{array} \qquad \begin{array}{r} 5 \\ + 3 \\ \hline 8 \end{array}$$

Example 2

Solve 4 + 7 =

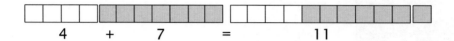

$$4 \quad + \quad 7 \quad = \quad 11$$

4 + 7 = 11

$$\begin{array}{r} 4 \\ + 7 \\ \hline 11 \end{array} \qquad \begin{array}{r} 7 \\ + 4 \\ \hline 11 \end{array}$$

7 + 4 = 11

Example 3

Solve 5 + 7 =

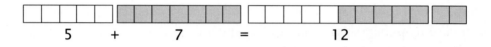

$$5 \quad + \quad 7 \quad = \quad 12$$

5 + 7 = 12

$$\begin{array}{r} 5 \\ + 7 \\ \hline 12 \end{array} \qquad \begin{array}{r} 7 \\ + 5 \\ \hline 12 \end{array}$$

7 + 5 = 12

This is the end of the individual addition facts. Please make sure the facts are all mastered before moving ahead to the next lesson. Having these facts under their belt will give confidence and let students focus on the new material without continually backtracking and doing too many things at the same time. Take whatever time students need for mastery to occur.

You did it! Congratulations on this accomplishment. After doing such a good job with addition, you will find that subtraction is a breeze. Wonderful job!

0 + 0	0 + 1	0 + 2	0 + 3	0 + 4	0 + 5	0 + 6	0 + 7	0 + 8	0 + 9
1 + 0	1 + 1	1 + 2	1 + 3	1 + 4	1 + 5	1 + 6	1 + 7	1 + 8	1 + 9
2 + 0	2 + 1	2 + 2	2 + 3	2 + 4	2 + 5	2 + 6	2 + 7	2 + 8	2 + 9
3 + 0	3 + 1	3 + 2	3 + 3	3 + 4	3 + 5	3 + 6	3 + 7	3 + 8	3 + 9
4 + 0	4 + 1	4 + 2	4 + 3	4 + 4	4 + 5	4 + 6	4 + 7	4 + 8	4 + 9
5 + 0	5 + 1	5 + 2	5 + 3	5 + 4	5 + 5	5 + 6	5 + 7	5 + 8	5 + 9
6 + 0	6 + 1	6 + 2	6 + 3	6 + 4	6 + 5	6 + 6	6 + 7	6 + 8	6 + 9
7 + 0	7 + 1	7 + 2	7 + 3	7 + 4	7 + 5	7 + 6	7 + 7	7 + 8	7 + 9
8 + 0	8 + 1	8 + 2	8 + 3	8 + 4	8 + 5	8 + 6	8 + 7	8 + 8	8 + 9
9 + 0	9 + 1	9 + 2	9 + 3	9 + 4	9 + 5	9 + 6	9 + 7	9 + 8	9 + 9

Teaching Tip

If you have a student who learns best when moving, try this tip. Take a child's ball and write the numbers 0–9 on it with an indelible marker. Toss the ball to your child and have him or her add the numbers that his thumbs are touching.

This is a tip from a mom on the Yahoo Math-U-See Users Loop. You can find a link to this group by going to mathusee.ca and choosing "E-Sources." Scroll down to find several interesting links. There is a list of games in the file section of the Yahoo group, and you can search the messages for more ideas.

Introduction to Subtraction

After we've mastered place value and all the addition facts, we are ready for subtraction. *Subtraction* is the opposite, or inverse, of addition. If you know how to add (2 + 3 = 5), and how to solve for an unknown (X + 2 = 5 and X + 3 = 5), then subtraction will follow easily. Rather than teach another complete set of facts, we will relate subtraction to these two previously mastered skills. If these skills are not mastered, please go back and spend whatever time is necessary until they are. Every subtraction problem can be rewritten and rephrased as an addition problem. We can read the example 5 – 2 = ? as "What number plus 2 is the same as 5?" This is identical to X + 2 = 5. You can see this with the blocks in example 1.

The answer to a subtraction problem is called the ***difference***. Instead of focusing on "taking away" or "minusing," focus on the difference between the two numbers being subtracted. This is why, instead of taking away, we can add up.

Start by pushing the blocks end to end as you would for an addition problem. (See example 1 on the next page.) Since subtraction is the opposite of addition, instead of leaving the blocks in that position, invert the two bar and place it on top of the five bar. The dark blocks in the picture represent the hollow side of the block. When the hollow side is showing, it means "take away" or "minus" or "owe." One parent commented that you are "in the hole" when the hollow side is showing. Make a real problem by saying, "I have five dollars and I owe the paper boy two dollars. How much do I have left?"

The symbol for subtraction is a single line. When making the problem by inverting the bottom number and placing it on the top number, say "difference between." You could envision the single line denoting subtraction as an arrow pointing out the "difference between."

Example 1

Solve 5 – 2 or

Step 1   Rephrase as an addition problem.

"Five minus two" means   5

"What plus two is the same as five?"   ↗ 2

Step 2   Rewrite as solving for an unknown.   X + 2 = 5

Step 3   **Step 4**

Build as an addition problem.   Invert and reposition.

   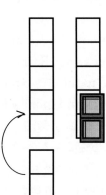

Step 5   Solve and write.

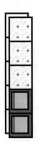   We see that 3 + 2 = 5,   5

thus 5 - 2 = 3.   – 2

                                                3

Example 2

Solve 7 – 3 or
$$\begin{array}{r} 7 \\ -3 \\ \hline \end{array}$$

Step 1   Rephrase as an addition problem.

"Seven minus three" means
"What plus three is the same as seven?"

Step 2   Rewrite as solving for an unknown.   X + 3 = 7

Step 3   **Step 4**
Build as an addition problem.   Invert and reposition.

   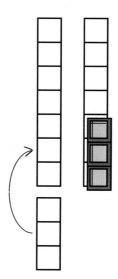

Step 5   Solve and write.

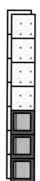

We see that 4 + 3 = 7, $\begin{array}{r} 7 \\ -\ 3 \\ \hline 4 \end{array}$
thus 7 - 3 = 4.

In this lesson, work on rewriting a subtraction problem as an addition problem. Use the blocks to show how subtraction is the inverse of addition. Help the student see how each problem is solved by adding up. Now we see why it is so important to have the addition facts mastered at this point.

Remind the students that they have already been subtracting as they solved for an unknown.

That is one of the main reasons we did that exercise. Granted, it lays a foundation for algebra and reviews addition facts, but the main purpose is to prepare them for subtraction. This should be an encouragement for those who have worked hard at learning this skill. It was not in vain!

Mental Math

Here are some more questions to read to your student. All of these review addition. You may shorten these if your student is not yet ready for the longer mental math questions.

1. One plus two, plus three, plus four equals what number? (10)

2. Two plus two, plus one, plus two equals what number? (7)

3. Three plus one, plus four, plus one equals what number? (9)

4. Eight plus zero, plus one, plus three equals what number? (12)

5. Five plus one, plus one, plus five equals what number? (12)

6. Five plus four, plus zero, plus seven equals what number? (16)

7. Two plus two, plus two, plus two equals what number? (8)

8. Three plus four, plus one, plus five equals what number? (13)

9. Two plus three, plus two, plus three equals what number? (10)

10. Zero plus one, plus five, plus two equals what number? (8)

LESSON 19

Subtraction: −1 and −0

As with addition, we'll begin with the simpler facts and move on from there. The first facts to be learned are the zero facts. If I have five dollars and I owe five dollars, how many dollars do I have? The answer is zero or nothing. The problem is written as 5 - 5 = 0. Look at example 1 to see it worked through. Before teaching subtraction by one, review counting backwards by one with the blocks arranged from one to nine as we did when adding nine in lesson 9.

Example 1

Solve 5 - 5 or $\begin{array}{r} 5 \\ -5 \\ \hline \end{array}$

Step 1   Rephrase as an addition problem.

"Five minus five" means
"What plus five is the same as five?"

Step 2   Rewrite as solving for an unknown.

$$X + 5 = 5$$

Step 3
Build as an addition problem.

Step 4
Invert and reposition.

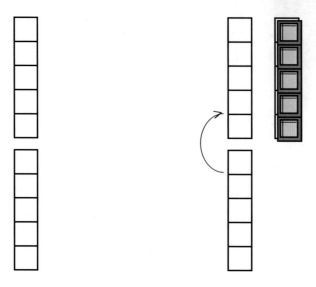

Step 5 Solve and write.

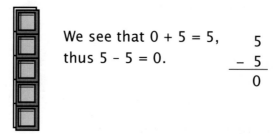

We see that 0 + 5 = 5,
thus 5 – 5 = 0.

$$\begin{array}{r} 5 \\ -\ 5 \\ \hline 0 \end{array}$$

Subtraction is not commutative. We see that 5 - 3 is not the same as 3 - 5. Addition *is* commutative, so 5 + 3 is the same as 3 + 5. However, when we rewrite a subtraction problem as an addition problem, we can tap into the commutative property of addition. In the problem 5 - 3 = 2 we can switch the 2 and the 3, since we are adding up, and adding is commutative. Notice that 2 + 3 = 5 is just the same as 3 + 2 = 5. A *corollary* is a statement written in a different form that is true because the original statement is true. You can use the word "cousin" with the student if you wish. The corollary to example 1 where 5 - 5 = 0 is 5 - 0 = 5. Notice this as we cover subtraction by one.

The prerequisite for learning how to find a difference of one, or the one facts, is learning how to add by one. Study example 2 and remember that 4 - 3 = 1 is the same as 4 - 1 = 3 when we are adding up.

Example 2

Solve 4 – 3 or   4
           – 3

Step 1   Rephrase as an addition problem.

"Four minus three" means
"What plus three is the same as four?"

Step 2   Rewrite as solving for an unknown.

$$X + 3 = 4$$

Step 3
Build as an addition problem.

Step 4
Invert and reposition.

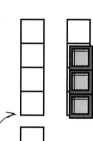

Step 5   Solve and write.

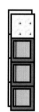

We see that 1 + 3 = 4,
thus 4 – 3 = 1.

      4
   – 3
      1

Step 5 The corollary to example 2.
(again)

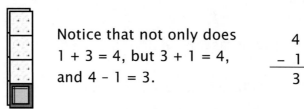

Notice that not only does
1 + 3 = 4, but 3 + 1 = 4,
and 4 - 1 = 3.

$$\begin{array}{r} 4 \\ -\ 1 \\ \hline 3 \end{array}$$

Because of the commutative property, when we learn the zero facts, which are in the first column and written vertically, we also learn the first row, written horizontally. So also for the one facts, where we learn the second column as well as the second row. Make a habit of encouraging the student by showing what we are learning lesson by lesson. There is a chart for the student after lesson 19 in the student text.

0 - 0	1 - 1	2 - 2	3 - 3	4 - 4	5 - 5	6 - 6	7 - 7	8 - 8	9 - 9
1 - 0	2 - 1	3 - 2	4 - 3	5 - 4	6 - 5	7 - 6	8 - 7	9 - 8	10 - 9
2 - 0	3 - 1	4 - 2	5 - 3	6 - 4	7 - 5	8 - 6	9 - 7	10 - 8	11 - 9
3 - 0	4 - 1	5 - 2	6 - 3	7 - 4	8 - 5	9 - 6	10 - 7	11 - 8	12 - 9
4 - 0	5 - 1	6 - 2	7 - 3	8 - 4	9 - 5	10 - 6	11 - 7	12 - 8	13 - 9
5 - 0	6 - 1	7 - 2	8 - 3	9 - 4	10 - 5	11 - 6	12 - 7	13 - 8	14 - 9
6 - 0	7 - 1	8 - 2	9 - 3	10 - 4	11 - 5	12 - 6	13 - 7	14 - 8	15 - 9
7 - 0	8 - 1	9 - 2	10 - 3	11 - 4	12 - 5	13 - 6	14 - 7	15 - 8	16 - 9
8 - 0	9 - 1	10 - 2	11 - 3	12 - 4	13 - 5	14 - 6	15 - 7	16 - 8	17 - 9
9 - 0	10 - 1	11 - 2	12 - 3	13 - 4	14 - 5	15 - 6	16 - 7	17 - 8	18 - 9

Subtraction Facts Sheet

0 − 0	1 − 1	2 − 2	3 − 3	4 − 4	5 − 5	6 − 6	7 − 7	8 − 8	9 − 9
1 − 0	2 − 1	3 − 2	4 − 3	5 − 4	6 − 5	7 − 6	8 − 7	9 − 8	10 − 9
2 − 0	3 − 1	4 − 2	5 − 3	6 − 4	7 − 5	8 − 6	9 − 7	10 − 8	11 − 9
3 − 0	4 − 1	5 − 2	6 − 3	7 − 4	8 − 5	9 − 6	10 − 7	11 − 8	12 − 9
4 − 0	5 − 1	6 − 2	7 − 3	8 − 4	9 − 5	10 − 6	11 − 7	12 − 8	13 − 9
5 − 0	6 − 1	7 − 2	8 − 3	9 − 4	10 − 5	11 − 6	12 − 7	13 − 8	14 − 9
6 − 0	7 − 1	8 − 2	9 − 3	10 − 4	11 − 5	12 − 6	13 − 7	14 − 8	15 − 9
7 − 0	8 − 1	9 − 2	10 − 3	11 − 4	12 − 5	13 − 6	14 − 7	15 − 8	16 − 9
8 − 0	9 − 1	10 − 2	11 − 3	12 − 4	13 − 5	14 − 6	15 − 7	16 − 8	17 − 9
9 − 0	10 − 1	11 − 2	12 − 3	13 − 4	14 − 5	15 − 6	16 − 7	17 − 8	18 − 9

Subtraction: −2

In this lesson we are learning to subtract by two. Because of what we know about the commutative property, this lesson also includes those problems with a difference of two. Example 1 shows minus two, and example 2 shows the same problem with a difference of two. In a subtraction problem the top number is called the *minuend* and the bottom number is the *subtrahend*. See figure 1.

Figure 1

$$
\begin{array}{r}
7 \\
-2 \\
\hline
5
\end{array}
\quad
\begin{array}{l}
\text{minuend} \\
\text{subtrahend} \\
\text{difference}
\end{array}
$$

Example 1

Solve 7 − 2 or
$$
\begin{array}{r}
7 \\
-2 \\
\hline
\end{array}
$$

Step 1   Rephrase as an addition problem.

"Seven minus two" means
"What plus two is the same as seven?"

Step 2   Rewrite as solving for an unknown.

X + 2 = 7

Step 3
Build as an addition problem.

Step 4
Invert and reposition.

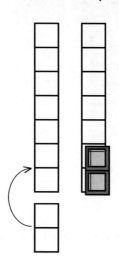

Step 5   Solve and write.

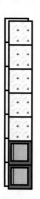

We see that 2 + 5 = 7,   7
thus 7 - 2 = 5.   – 2
                          ___
                            5

Example 1
Solve 7 – 5 or   7
                  –5
                  ___

Step 1 and 2   Rephrase and rewrite.

"Seven minus five" means
"What plus five is the same as seven?"   X + 5 = 7

Step 3
Build as an addition problem.

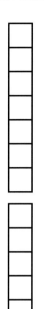

Step 4
Invert and reposition.

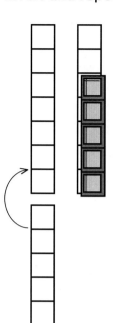

Step 5   Solve and write.

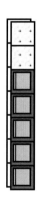

We see that 5 + 2 = 7,
thus 7 - 5 = 2.

$$\begin{array}{r} 7 \\ -\ 5 \\ \hline 2 \end{array}$$

Because of the commutative property, when we learn the two facts, which are in the third column, we also learn the facts with a difference of two in the third row. If you add all the shaded ones in the chart, you will see that we have already learned over half of the facts. Fifty-one mastered and 49 to go. Congratulations!

0 - 0	1 - 1	2 - 2	3 - 3	4 - 4	5 - 5	6 - 6	7 - 7	8 - 8	9 - 9
1 - 0	2 - 1	3 - 2	4 - 3	5 - 4	6 - 5	7 - 6	8 - 7	9 - 8	10 - 9
2 - 0	3 - 1	4 - 2	5 - 3	6 - 4	7 - 5	8 - 6	9 - 7	10 - 8	11 - 9
3 - 0	4 - 1	5 - 2	6 - 3	7 - 4	8 - 5	9 - 6	10 - 7	11 - 8	12 - 9
4 - 0	5 - 1	6 - 2	7 - 3	8 - 4	9 - 5	10 - 6	11 - 7	12 - 8	13 - 9
5 - 0	6 - 1	7 - 2	8 - 3	9 - 4	10 - 5	11 - 6	12 - 7	13 - 8	14 - 9
6 - 0	7 - 1	8 - 2	9 - 3	10 - 4	11 - 5	12 - 6	13 - 7	14 - 8	15 - 9
7 - 0	8 - 1	9 - 2	10 - 3	11 - 4	12 - 5	13 - 6	14 - 7	15 - 8	16 - 9
8 - 0	9 - 1	10 - 2	11 - 3	12 - 4	13 - 5	14 - 6	15 - 7	16 - 8	17 - 9
9 - 0	10 - 1	11 - 2	12 - 3	13 - 4	14 - 5	15 - 6	16 - 7	17 - 8	18 - 9

Teaching Tip

Don't forget the importance of applying math to everyday life. Ask questions as you shop, cook, and do daily chores.

LESSON 21

Subtraction: –9

Subtracting by nine, which used to be one of the toughest sets of problems, can now be one of the easiest. It is simply adding by one. This is a two-step problem. The first step is to make 10. Continue adding up to the number in the units place. The blocks clearly show this. We inserted an outline of a 10 to show both steps.

Example 1

$$\begin{array}{r} 13 \\ -9 \\ \hline 4 \end{array}$$

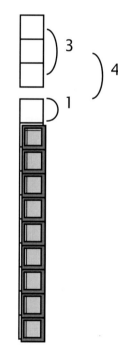

$$\begin{array}{r} 13 \\ 10 \\ -9 \\ \hline 4 \end{array} \begin{array}{l} 3 \\ 1 \end{array}$$

10 plus what equals 13?
The answer is 3.
9 plus what equals 10?
The answer is 1.

The difference
(or distance between)
9 and 13 is 1 + 3, or 4.

Remember how we learned to add by nine? First we vacuumed one from the number and added 10. In subtraction, the opposite or inverse of addition, we add up by one instead of vacuuming or taking away one.

Example 2

$$
\begin{array}{r}
15 \\
-9 \\
\hline
\end{array}
$$

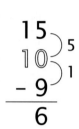

10 plus what equals 15?
The answer is 5.
9 plus what equals 10?
The answer is 1.

The difference
(or distance between)
9 and 15 is 1 + 5, or 6.

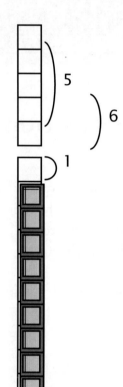

Example 3

16
−9
‾‾‾

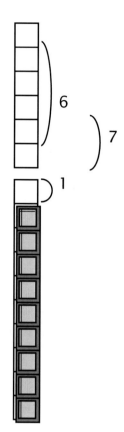

10 plus what equals 16?
The answer is 6.
9 plus what equals 10?
The answer is 1.

16) 6
10)
− 9) 1
‾‾‾
7

The difference
(or distance between)
9 and 16 is 1 + 6, or 7.

Now we have learned 58 facts with just 42 to go. Keep up the good work!

0 - 0	1 - 1	2 - 2	3 - 3	4 - 4	5 - 5	6 - 6	7 - 7	8 - 8	9 - 9
1 - 0	2 - 1	3 - 2	4 - 3	5 - 4	6 - 5	7 - 6	8 - 7	9 - 8	10 - 9
2 - 0	3 - 1	4 - 2	5 - 3	6 - 4	7 - 5	8 - 6	9 - 7	10 - 8	11 - 9
3 - 0	4 - 1	5 - 2	6 - 3	7 - 4	8 - 5	9 - 6	10 - 7	11 - 8	12 - 9
4 - 0	5 - 1	6 - 2	7 - 3	8 - 4	9 - 5	10 - 6	11 - 7	12 - 8	13 - 9
5 - 0	6 - 1	7 - 2	8 - 3	9 - 4	10 - 5	11 - 6	12 - 7	13 - 8	14 - 9
6 - 0	7 - 1	8 - 2	9 - 3	10 - 4	11 - 5	12 - 6	13 - 7	14 - 8	15 - 9
7 - 0	8 - 1	9 - 2	10 - 3	11 - 4	12 - 5	13 - 6	14 - 7	15 - 8	16 - 9
8 - 0	9 - 1	10 - 2	11 - 3	12 - 4	13 - 5	14 - 6	15 - 7	16 - 8	17 - 9
9 - 0	10 - 1	11 - 2	12 - 3	13 - 4	14 - 5	15 - 6	16 - 7	17 - 8	18 - 9

Mental Math

Here are some more questions to read to your student. All of these review addition. You may shorten these if your student is not yet ready for the longer questions.

1. Four plus two, plus two, plus seven equals what number? (15)
2. Five plus three, plus one, plus three equals what number? (12)
3. Seven plus one, plus two, plus one equals what number? (11)
4. Three plus four, plus two, plus zero equals what number? (9)
5. One plus five, plus two, plus six equals what number? (14)
6. Zero plus one, plus three, plus three equals what number? (7)
7. Three plus three, plus three, plus three equals what number? (12)
8. Two plus four, plus one, plus nine equals what number? (16)
9. Three plus five, plus two, plus four equals what number? (14)
10. Four plus zero, plus eight, plus one equals what number? (13)
11. Six plus two, plus one, plus one equals what number? (10)
12. Three plus three, plus one, plus eight equals what number? (15)

LESSON 22

Subtraction: −8

Subtracting by eight is just like subtracting by nine, except that we need to add two when adding up. It is a two-step problem as well. The first step is to make 10. Then continue adding up to the number in the units place. When we learned to add by eight, we vacuumed two from the number, and then added 10. In subtraction by eight, we add up by two, instead of vacuuming two.

Example 1

$$
\begin{array}{r}
13 \\
-8 \\
\end{array}
$$

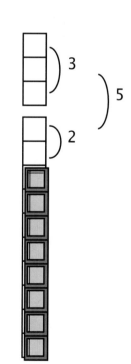

$$
\begin{array}{r}
13 \\
10 \\
-8 \\
\hline
5 \\
\end{array}
$$

10 plus what equals 13?
The answer is 3.
8 plus what equals 10?
The answer is 2.

The difference between
8 and 13 is 2 + 3, or 5.

Example 2

$$\begin{array}{r} 11 \\ -8 \\ \hline \end{array}$$

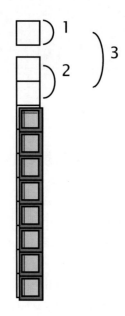

$$\begin{array}{r} 11 \\ 10 \\ -8 \\ \hline 3 \end{array}$$

10 plus what equals 11?
The answer is 1.
8 plus what equals 10?
The answer is 2.

The difference between
8 and 11 is 2 + 1, or 3.

Example 3

$$\begin{array}{r} 15 \\ -8 \\ \hline \end{array}$$

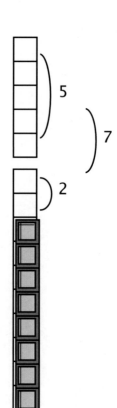

$$\begin{array}{r} 15 \\ 10 \\ -8 \\ \hline 7 \end{array}$$

10 plus what equals 15?
The answer is 5.
8 plus what equals 10?
The answer is 2.

The difference between
8 and 15 is 2 + 5, or 7.

With the eights mastered, you have now learned 65 facts, with just 35 to go. Notice how the chart is almost all shaded. Be encouraged!

0 – 0	1 – 1	2 – 2	3 – 3	4 – 4	5 – 5	6 – 6	7 – 7	8 – 8	9 – 9
1 – 0	2 – 1	3 – 2	4 – 3	5 – 4	6 – 5	7 – 6	8 – 7	9 – 8	10 – 9
2 – 0	3 – 1	4 – 2	5 – 3	6 – 4	7 – 5	8 – 6	9 – 7	10 – 8	11 – 9
3 – 0	4 – 1	5 – 2	6 – 3	7 – 4	8 – 5	9 – 6	10 – 7	11 – 8	12 – 9
4 – 0	5 – 1	6 – 2	7 – 3	8 – 4	9 – 5	10 – 6	11 – 7	12 – 8	13 – 9
5 – 0	6 – 1	7 – 2	8 – 3	9 – 4	10 – 5	11 – 6	12 – 7	13 – 8	14 – 9
6 – 0	7 – 1	8 – 2	9 – 3	10 – 4	11 – 5	12 – 6	13 – 7	14 – 8	15 – 9
7 – 0	8 – 1	9 – 2	10 – 3	11 – 4	12 – 5	13 – 6	14 – 7	15 – 8	16 – 9
8 – 0	9 – 1	10 – 2	11 – 3	12 – 4	13 – 5	14 – 6	15 – 7	16 – 8	17 – 9
9 – 0	10 – 1	11 – 2	12 – 3	13 – 4	14 – 5	15 – 6	16 – 7	17 – 8	18 – 9

Teaching Tip

If a student has gotten into the habit of counting on fingers, it can be very hard to break. Some students know their facts but lack confidence. Here is a strategy that has helped some parents in this situation. Put the blocks on a different table than the one where the student is working. Tell the student that he or she may not use fingers. The blocks may be used if the student is unsure of an answer. However, getting up to go get the blocks is a nuisance. For many students this is a way to encourage them to use what they really do know, while giving them a way to find the answer if they get stuck.

Subtraction: Doubles

The facts have been easy so far, and these may be the easiest yet. Adding the doubles comes pretty quickly to many students. We hope these will be learned just as readily by your student. The difficult fact for adding is 7 + 7, but if you've learned that one, then this lesson will be a breeze.

Example 1
Solve 10 − 5.

$$
\begin{array}{r} 10 \\ -5 \\ \hline \end{array}
$$
"Ten minus five" means
"What plus five is the same as ten?"   X + 5 = 10

$$
\begin{array}{r} 10 \\ -5 \\ \hline 5 \end{array}
$$
Five plus five equals ten.   5 + 5 = 10

Example 2

Solve 8 - 4.

8
−4

"Eight minus four" means
"What plus four is the same as eight?"   W + 4 = 8

8
−4
4

Four plus four equals eight.   4 + 4 = 8

Example 3

Solve 14 − 7.

14
−7

"Fourteen minus seven" means
"What plus seven is equal to fourteen?" Y + 7 =14

14
−7
7

Seven plus seven equals fourteen.

7 + 7 =14

There are five new doubles facts, which makes 70 down and 30 to go. Notice that the doubles go diagonally on the chart. Keep on keeping on!

0 – 0	1 – 1	2 – 2	3 – 3	4 – 4	5 – 5	6 – 6	7 – 7	8 – 8	9 – 9
1 – 0	2 – 1	3 – 2	4 – 3	5 – 4	6 – 5	7 – 6	8 – 7	9 – 8	10 – 9
2 – 0	3 – 1	4 – 2	5 – 3	6 – 4	7 – 5	8 – 6	9 – 7	10 – 8	11 – 9
3 – 0	4 – 1	5 – 2	6 – 3	7 – 4	8 – 5	9 – 6	10 – 7	11 – 8	12 – 9
4 – 0	5 – 1	6 – 2	7 – 3	8 – 4	9 – 5	10 – 6	11 – 7	12 – 8	13 – 9
5 – 0	6 – 1	7 – 2	8 – 3	9 – 4	10 – 5	11 – 6	12 – 7	13 – 8	14 – 9
6 – 0	7 – 1	8 – 2	9 – 3	10 – 4	11 – 5	12 – 6	13 – 7	14 – 8	15 – 9
7 – 0	8 – 1	9 – 2	10 – 3	11 – 4	12 – 5	13 – 6	14 – 7	15 – 8	16 – 9
8 – 0	9 – 1	10 – 2	11 – 3	12 – 4	13 – 5	14 – 6	15 – 7	16 – 8	17 – 9
9 – 0	10 – 1	11 – 2	12 – 3	13 – 4	14 – 5	15 – 6	16 – 7	17 – 8	18 – 9

Subtraction: Making 10

The facts we cover in this lesson are directly related to the addition facts, just as all the other subtraction facts have been. Making the 10 family is the foundation for this set of subtraction facts. We know that $1 + 9$, $2 + 8$, $3 + 7$, $4 + 6$, and $5 + 5$ are all the ways to make 10. We learned these facts by stacking the unit bars two in a row on top of the 10 bar. This is the inverse. Given one of the blocks, what combined with it will make 10? Study the examples and have fun making 10. There are four new facts in this lesson.

Example 1
Solve 10 - 3.

$$\begin{array}{r} 10 \\ -3 \\ \hline \end{array}$$ "Ten minus three" means
"What plus three is the same as ten?"

$$P + 3 = 10$$

$$\begin{array}{r} 10 \\ -3 \\ \hline 7 \end{array}$$ Seven plus three equals ten.

$$7 + 3 = 10$$

Example 2
Solve 10 – 4.

10
–4

"Ten minus four" means
"What plus four is the same as ten?"   G + 4 = 10

10
–4
6

Six plus four equals ten.   6 + 4 = 10

ALPHA

Example 3

Solve 10 – 7.

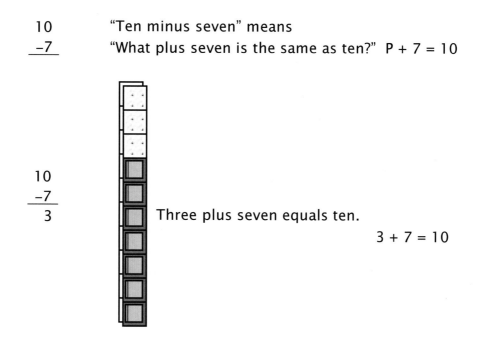

10
–7

"Ten minus seven" means
"What plus seven is the same as ten?" P + 7 = 10

10
–7
___
3

Three plus seven equals ten.

3 + 7 = 10

Example 3 is the corollary or cousin of example 1. Do you see it?

There are four new facts. These appear diagonally like the doubles. We have conquered 74 facts and 26 more are ready to be conquered.

0 – 0	1 – 1	2 – 2	3 – 3	4 – 4	5 – 5	6 – 6	7 – 7	8 – 8	9 – 9
1 – 0	2 – 1	3 – 2	4 – 3	5 – 4	6 – 5	7 – 6	8 – 7	9 – 8	10 – 9
2 – 0	3 – 1	4 – 2	5 – 3	6 – 4	7 – 5	8 – 6	9 – 7	10 – 8	11 – 9
3 – 0	4 – 1	5 – 2	6 – 3	7 – 4	8 – 5	9 – 6	10 – 7	11 – 8	12 – 9
4 – 0	5 – 1	6 – 2	7 – 3	8 – 4	9 – 5	10 – 6	11 – 7	12 – 8	13 – 9
5 – 0	6 – 1	7 – 2	8 – 3	9 – 4	10 – 5	11 – 6	12 – 7	13 – 8	14 – 9
6 – 0	7 – 1	8 – 2	9 – 3	10 – 4	11 – 5	12 – 6	13 – 7	14 – 8	15 – 9
7 – 0	8 – 1	9 – 2	10 – 3	11 – 4	12 – 5	13 – 6	14 – 7	15 – 8	16 – 9
8 – 0	9 – 1	10 – 2	11 – 3	12 – 4	13 – 5	14 – 6	15 – 7	16 – 8	17 – 9
9 – 0	10 – 1	11 – 2	12 – 3	13 – 4	14 – 5	15 – 6	16 – 7	17 – 8	18 – 9

Mental Math

Here are some more questions to read to your student. These combine addition and subtraction. You may need to go slowly with these at first.

1. Three plus four, minus two, equals what number? (5)

2. Six minus one, plus five, equals what number? (10)

3. One plus eight, minus eight, equals what number? (1)

4. Four minus two, plus nine, equals what number? (11)

5. Nine minus seven, plus four, equals what number? (6)

6. Eight minus five, plus seven, equals what number? (10)

7. Three plus eight, minus four, equals what number? (7)

8. Seven plus seven, minus five, equals what number? (9)

9. Eleven minus three, plus five, equals what number? (13)

10. Fifteen minus eight, plus one, equals what number? (8)

LESSON 25

Subtraction: Making 9

Making the nine family is the foundation for this set of subtraction facts. We know that 1 + 8, 2 + 7, 3 + 6, and 4 + 5 are all ways to make nine.

There are four new facts in this lesson. We will learn 9 - 3 and its corollary 9 - 6, and 9 - 4 and its corollary, or cousin, 9 - 5.

Example 1
Solve 9 – 3.

$$\begin{array}{r} 9 \\ -3 \\ \hline \end{array}$$
"Nine minus three" means
"What plus three is the same as nine?"

$$R + 3 = 9$$

$$\begin{array}{r} 9 \\ -3 \\ \hline 6 \end{array}$$
Six plus three equals nine. $6 + 3 = 9$

Example 2

Solve 9 – 4.

$$\begin{array}{r} 9 \\ -4 \\ \hline \end{array}$$

"Nine minus four" means
"What plus four is the same as nine?"   R + 4 = 9

$$\begin{array}{r} 9 \\ -4 \\ \hline 5 \end{array}$$

Five plus four equals nine.   5 + 4 = 9

Example 3 is the corollary, or cousin, of example 2.

Example 3

Solve 9 – 5.

$$\begin{array}{r} 9 \\ -5 \\ \hline \end{array}$$

"Nine minus five" means
"What plus five is the same as nine?"   T + 5 = 9

$$\begin{array}{r} 9 \\ -5 \\ \hline 4 \end{array}$$

Four plus five equals nine.   4 + 5 = 9

There are four new nine facts. These appear diagonally right above the 10 family. Seventy-eight facts are mastered and 22 are ready for our expertise.

0-0	1-1	2-2	3-3	4-4	5-5	6-6	7-7	8-8	9-9
1-0	2-1	3-2	4-3	5-4	6-5	7-6	8-7	9-8	10-9
2-0	3-1	4-2	5-3	6-4	7-5	8-6	9-7	10-8	11-9
3-0	4-1	5-2	6-3	7-4	8-5	9-6	10-7	11-8	12-9
4-0	5-1	6-2	7-3	8-4	9-5	10-6	11-7	12-8	13-9
5-0	6-1	7-2	8-3	9-4	10-5	11-6	12-7	13-8	14-9
6-0	7-1	8-2	9-3	10-4	11-5	12-6	13-7	14-8	15-9
7-0	8-1	9-2	10-3	11-4	12-5	13-6	14-7	15-8	16-9
8-0	9-1	10-2	11-3	12-4	13-5	14-6	15-7	16-8	17-9
9-0	10-1	11-2	12-3	13-4	14-5	15-6	16-7	17-8	18-9

LESSON 26

Subtraction: Extras

When we learned these facts in addition, they were referred to as the extras because they didn't fit into a pattern or a family. There are four facts to be learned in this lesson, but as we've said many times before, because of the commutative property there are really only two facts. This lesson includes 7 - 4, 7 - 3, 8 - 5, and 8 - 3. These are the first subtraction facts learned without a family or some sort of easy pattern, so be sure you understand them before moving on.

Example 1
Solve 7 – 3.

$$
\begin{array}{r}
7 \\
-3 \\
\hline
\end{array}
$$

"Seven minus three" means
"What plus three is the same as seven?"

$$R + 3 = 7$$

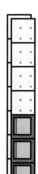

$$
\begin{array}{r}
7 \\
-3 \\
\hline
4
\end{array}
$$

Four plus three equals seven. $4 + 3 = 7$

Example 2

Solve 7 – 4.

7
–4
        "Seven minus four" means
        "What plus four is the same as seven?"

C + 4 = 7

7
–4
3
        Three plus four equals seven.   3 + 4 = 7

Example 2 is the cousin of example 1. The corollary of example 3 is 8 - 3 = 5.

Example 3

Solve 8 – 5.

8
–5
        "Eight minus five" means
        "What plus five is the same as eight?"

Q + 5 = 8

8
–5
3
        Three plus five equals eight.   3 + 5 = 8

We learned four new facts in this lesson. These appear in the corners above the 9 and 10 families. This lesson makes a grand total of 82 learned with only 18 to go.

0 - 0	1 - 1	2 - 2	3 - 3	4 - 4	5 - 5	6 - 6	7 - 7	8 - 8	9 - 9
1 - 0	2 - 1	3 - 2	4 - 3	5 - 4	6 - 5	7 - 6	8 - 7	9 - 8	10 - 9
2 - 0	3 - 1	4 - 2	5 - 3	6 - 4	7 - 5	8 - 6	9 - 7	10 - 8	11 - 9
3 - 0	4 - 1	5 - 2	6 - 3	7 - 4	8 - 5	9 - 6	10 - 7	11 - 8	12 - 9
4 - 0	5 - 1	6 - 2	7 - 3	8 - 4	9 - 5	10 - 6	11 - 7	12 - 8	13 - 9
5 - 0	6 - 1	7 - 2	8 - 3	9 - 4	10 - 5	11 - 6	12 - 7	13 - 8	14 - 9
6 - 0	7 - 1	8 - 2	9 - 3	10 - 4	11 - 5	12 - 6	13 - 7	14 - 8	15 - 9
7 - 0	8 - 1	9 - 2	10 - 3	11 - 4	12 - 5	13 - 6	14 - 7	15 - 8	16 - 9
8 - 0	9 - 1	10 - 2	11 - 3	12 - 4	13 - 5	14 - 6	15 - 7	16 - 8	17 - 9
9 - 0	10 - 1	11 - 2	12 - 3	13 - 4	14 - 5	15 - 6	16 - 7	17 - 8	18 - 9

Subtraction by 7, or Adding Up by 3

In the next four lessons the minuend or top number is a double-digit number. We are going to treat these as we did subtracting by eight and nine. This will be the two-step approach: first adding up to 10, and then adding the number in the units place to find the difference. We are assuming a thorough mastery of the 10 family for the remainder of the lessons dealing with subtraction facts. The facts to be learned are 11 - 7, 12 - 7, 13 - 7, 15 - 7, and 16 - 7. These are the toughest to be learned so far, so take your time. Instead of subtracting by seven we are adding up by three.

Example 1

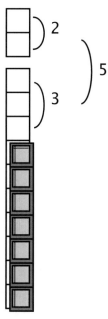

$$\begin{array}{r} 12 \\ -7 \\ \hline \end{array}$$

$$\begin{array}{r} 12 \\ 10 \\ -7 \\ \hline 5 \end{array}$$ 2 3

10 plus what equals 12?
The answer is 2.
7 plus what equals 10?
The answer is 3.

The difference between
7 and 12 is 3 + 2, or 5.

Example 2

13
−7

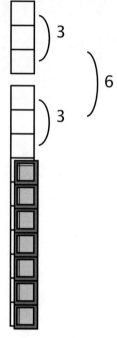

13
10 ⟩ 3
−7 ⟩ 3
──
6

10 plus what equals 13?
The answer is 3.
7 plus what equals 10?
The answer is 3.

The difference between
7 and 13 is 3 + 3, or 6.

Example 3

15
−7

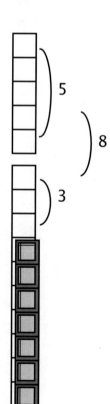

15
10 ⟩ 5
−7 ⟩ 3
──
8

10 plus what equals 15?
The answer is 5.
7 plus what equals 10?
The answer is 3.

The difference between
7 and 15 is 3 + 5, or 8.

With the five new facts in this lesson, 87 have been mastered and only 13 remain. The new chunk is in the minus seven column.

0 – 0	1 – 1	2 – 2	3 – 3	4 – 4	5 – 5	6 – 6	7 – 7	8 – 8	9 – 9
1 – 0	2 – 1	3 – 2	4 – 3	5 – 4	6 – 5	7 – 6	8 – 7	9 – 8	10 – 9
2 – 0	3 – 1	4 – 2	5 – 3	6 – 4	7 – 5	8 – 6	9 – 7	10 – 8	11 – 9
3 – 0	4 – 1	5 – 2	6 – 3	7 – 4	8 – 5	9 – 6	10 – 7	11 – 8	12 – 9
4 – 0	5 – 1	6 – 2	7 – 3	8 – 4	9 – 5	10 – 6	11 – 7	12 – 8	13 – 9
5 – 0	6 – 1	7 – 2	8 – 3	9 – 4	10 – 5	11 – 6	12 – 7	13 – 8	14 – 9
6 – 0	7 – 1	8 – 2	9 – 3	10 – 4	11 – 5	12 – 6	13 – 7	14 – 8	15 – 9
7 – 0	8 – 1	9 – 2	10 – 3	11 – 4	12 – 5	13 – 6	14 – 7	15 – 8	16 – 9
8 – 0	9 – 1	10 – 2	11 – 3	12 – 4	13 – 5	14 – 6	15 – 7	16 – 8	17 – 9
9 – 0	10 – 1	11 – 2	12 – 3	13 – 4	14 – 5	15 – 6	16 – 7	17 – 8	18 – 9

Mental Math

Here are some more questions to read to your student. These combine addition and subtraction. You may shorten these if your student is not yet ready for the longer questions.

1. One plus two, minus one, plus five, equals what number? (7)

2. Four plus one, minus zero, plus six, equals what number? (11)

3. Eight minus four, plus three, plus five, equals what number? (12)

4. Three plus nine, minus six, plus four, equals what number? (10)

5. Fourteen minus nine, minus one, plus three, equals what number? (7)

6. One plus nine, minus eight, plus nine, equals what number? (11)

7. Six plus six, minus six, minus six, equals what number? (0)

8. Seven plus five, plus zero, minus eight, equals what number? (4)

9. Eighteen minus nine, minus five, plus one, equals what number? (5)

10. Six plus two, minus seven, plus three, equals what number? (4)

Subtraction by 6, or Adding Up by 4

There are four facts to be learned here. They are 11 - 6, 13 - 6, 14 - 6, and 15 - 6.
As the title suggests, we could call these subtracting by six or adding up by four, as
we have observed with the blocks. Study these carefully and add them to the ones
you have already learned. They are not difficult when you use the blocks and think
about what you are doing.

Example 1

$$\begin{array}{r} 11 \\ -6 \\ \hline \end{array}$$

$$\begin{array}{r} 11 \\ 10 \\ -\ 6 \\ \hline 5 \end{array}$$

10 plus what equals 11?
The answer is 1.
6 plus what equals 10?
The answer is 4.

The difference between
6 and 11 is 4 + 1, or 5.

Example 2

13
−6
‾‾‾‾

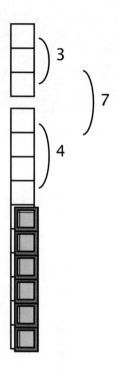

13
10) 3
− 6) 4
‾‾‾‾
7

10 plus what equals 13?
The answer is 3.
6 plus what equals 10?
The answer is 4.

The difference between
6 and 13 is 4 + 3, or 7.

Example 3

15
−6
‾‾‾‾

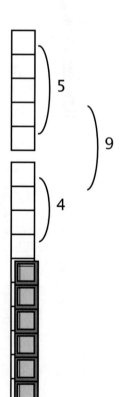

15
10) 5
− 6) 4
‾‾‾‾
9

10 plus what equals 15?
The answer is 5.
6 plus what equals 10?
The answer is 4.

The difference between
6 and 15 is 4 + 5, or 9.

These four new facts are in the minus six column. Ninety-one facts have been mastered, and we are counting down to the final nine.

0 - 0	1 - 1	2 - 2	3 - 3	4 - 4	5 - 5	6 - 6	7 - 7	8 - 8	9 - 9
1 - 0	2 - 1	3 - 2	4 - 3	5 - 4	6 - 5	7 - 6	8 - 7	9 - 8	10 - 9
2 - 0	3 - 1	4 - 2	5 - 3	6 - 4	7 - 5	8 - 6	9 - 7	10 - 8	11 - 9
3 - 0	4 - 1	5 - 2	6 - 3	7 - 4	8 - 5	9 - 6	10 - 7	11 - 8	12 - 9
4 - 0	5 - 1	6 - 2	7 - 3	8 - 4	9 - 5	10 - 6	11 - 7	12 - 8	13 - 9
5 - 0	6 - 1	7 - 2	8 - 3	9 - 4	10 - 5	11 - 6	12 - 7	13 - 8	14 - 9
6 - 0	7 - 1	8 - 2	9 - 3	10 - 4	11 - 5	12 - 6	13 - 7	14 - 8	15 - 9
7 - 0	8 - 1	9 - 2	10 - 3	11 - 4	12 - 5	13 - 6	14 - 7	15 - 8	16 - 9
8 - 0	9 - 1	10 - 2	11 - 3	12 - 4	13 - 5	14 - 6	15 - 7	16 - 8	17 - 9
9 - 0	10 - 1	11 - 2	12 - 3	13 - 4	14 - 5	15 - 6	16 - 7	17 - 8	18 - 9

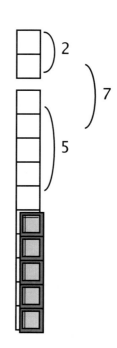

LESSON 29

Subtraction by 5, or Adding Up by 5

The four new facts are 11 - 5, 12 - 5, 13 - 5, and 14 - 5. As you've come to expect, we can refer to them as subtracting by five or adding up by five. Have fun memorizing these facts.

Example 1

$$\begin{array}{r} 12 \\ -5 \\ \hline \end{array}$$

$$\begin{array}{r} 12 \\ 10 \\ -5 \\ \hline 7 \end{array}\begin{array}{l} 2 \\ 5 \end{array}$$

10 plus what equals 12?
The answer is 2.
5 plus what equals 10?
The answer is 5.

The difference between 5 and 12 is 5 + 2, or 7.

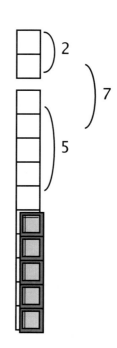

Example 2

13
−5

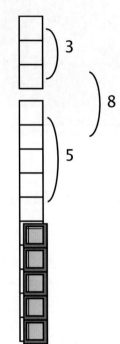

13⟩3
10⟨
−5⟩5
8

10 plus what equals 13?
The answer is 3.
5 plus what equals 10?
The answer is 5.

The difference between
5 and 13 is 5 + 3, or 8.

Example 3

14
−5

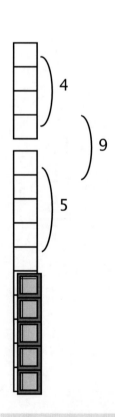

14⟩4
10⟨
−5⟩5
9

10 plus what equals 14?
The answer is 4.
5 plus what equals 10?
The answer is 5.

The difference between
5 and 14 is 5 + 4, or 9.

Having memorized these four facts, we have mastered 95 facts and are down to the final five. The four new facts appear in the minus five column.

0 – 0	1 – 1	2 – 2	3 – 3	4 – 4	5 – 5	6 – 6	7 – 7	8 – 8	9 – 9
1 – 0	2 – 1	3 – 2	4 – 3	5 – 4	6 – 5	7 – 6	8 – 7	9 – 8	10 – 9
2 – 0	3 – 1	4 – 2	5 – 3	6 – 4	7 – 5	8 – 6	9 – 7	10 – 8	11 – 9
3 – 0	4 – 1	5 – 2	6 – 3	7 – 4	8 – 5	9 – 6	10 – 7	11 – 8	12 – 9
4 – 0	5 – 1	6 – 2	7 – 3	8 – 4	9 – 5	10 – 6	11 – 7	12 – 8	13 – 9
5 – 0	6 – 1	7 – 2	8 – 3	9 – 4	10 – 5	11 – 6	12 – 7	13 – 8	14 – 9
6 – 0	7 – 1	8 – 2	9 – 3	10 – 4	11 – 5	12 – 6	13 – 7	14 – 8	15 – 9
7 – 0	8 – 1	9 – 2	10 – 3	11 – 4	12 – 5	13 – 6	14 – 7	15 – 8	16 – 9
8 – 0	9 – 1	10 – 2	11 – 3	12 – 4	13 – 5	14 – 6	15 – 7	16 – 8	17 – 9
9 – 0	10 – 1	11 – 2	12 – 3	13 – 4	14 – 5	15 – 6	16 – 7	17 – 8	18 – 9

LESSON 30

Subtraction by 3 and 4
Or Adding Up by 6 and 7

Five more facts and we are done. These seem more difficult than most, but they are not too hard when we know how to add. The facts are 11 - 3, 12 - 3, 11 - 4, 12 - 4, and 13 - 4. I'm still convinced that adding up is the clearest way to learn these facts, but when all else fails, simply memorize them.

Example 1

$$\begin{array}{r} 12 \\ -4 \\ \hline \end{array}$$

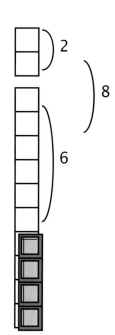

$$\begin{array}{r} 12 \\ 10 \\ -4 \\ \hline 8 \end{array} \begin{array}{l} 2 \\ 6 \end{array}$$

10 plus what equals 12?
The answer is 2.
4 plus what equals 10?
The answer is 6.

The difference between
4 and 12 is 6 + 2, or 8.

Example 2

13
−4
———

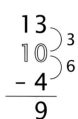

10 plus what equals 13?
The answer is 3.
4 plus what equals 10?
The answer is 6.

The difference between
4 and 13 is 6 + 3, or 9.

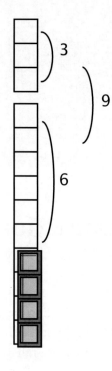

Example 3

12
−3
———

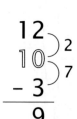

10 plus what equals 12?
The answer is 2.
3 plus what equals 10?
The answer is 7.

The difference between
3 and 12 is 7 + 2, or 9.

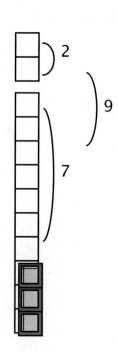

You made it! What a whiz you are! Congratulations! All 100 subtraction facts have been learned.

0-0	1-1	2-2	3-3	4-4	5-5	6-6	7-7	8-8	9-9
1-0	2-1	3-2	4-3	5-4	6-5	7-6	8-7	9-8	10-9
2-0	3-1	4-2	5-3	6-4	7-5	8-6	9-7	10-8	11-9
3-0	4-1	5-2	6-3	7-4	8-5	9-6	10-7	11-8	12-9
4-0	5-1	6-2	7-3	8-4	9-5	10-6	11-7	12-8	13-9
5-0	6-1	7-2	8-3	9-4	10-5	11-6	12-7	13-8	14-9
6-0	7-1	8-2	9-3	10-4	11-5	12-6	13-7	14-8	15-9
7-0	8-1	9-2	10-3	11-4	12-5	13-6	14-7	15-8	16-9
8-0	9-1	10-2	11-3	12-4	13-5	14-6	15-7	16-8	17-9
9-0	10-1	11-2	12-3	13-4	14-5	15-6	16-7	17-8	18-9

APPENDIX A

Telling Time: Minutes

When the student has mastered skip counting by fives, he is ready to learn how to tell time. To teach telling time with a clock that is not digital can be a challenge. We'll begin by taking six 10 bars and explaining that there are 60 minutes in one hour. Next replace each 10 bar with two five bars. If you don't have 12 five bars, use five units, or a four and one bar, or a three and two bar. Arrange your 12 groups of five in a circle (really a dodecagon, or 12-sided polygon) so that your 60 minutes are in the shape of a clock. Starting at the top, begin skip counting by fives and go around the clock. 5-10-15 . . . 55-60.

Choose any long bar, turn it on its side so that it is smooth, and use that as your minute hand. Point it at different areas, and beginning at the top, count your minutes. Using all of the blocks in the starter box of blocks, you can make this clock by using various combinations for fives (five unit pieces, or a two and a three, or a four and a unit). There is a removable clock template for you at the end of the student book.

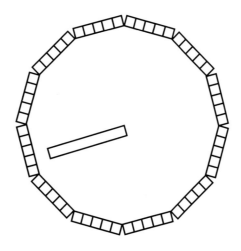

To help the students see the progression of the minutes, build several partial clocks as in examples 1 and 2. Count the minutes by beginning at the top and moving around to the right, or clockwise.

Example 1
Count the minutes.
5-10, so 10 minutes

Example 2
Count the minutes.
5-10-15, so 15 minutes

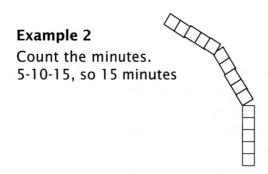

APPENDIX B

Telling Time: Hours

Once the minutes are mastered, we can add the hours by placing a green unit bar at the end of the first five bar (outside the circle) pointing away from the centre of the clock. (See the diagram on the next page.) To distinguish between the minutes and hours, I leave the minutes unit bars right side up, but the hours I place upside down with the hollow side showing. You can still see the colour and how many hours there are, but it helps to distinguish the minutes from the hours. Place your orange bar (upside down so the hollow side is showing) at the end of the second five bar. Continue this process with all the unit bars through 12. Choose a smaller unit bar than your minute hand for an hour hand. Turn it upside down so the student makes the connection between the hour hand and the hours, since both are upside down with the hollow side showing.

Now position the hour hand so that it points between the two and the three. This is the critical point for telling time. Is it two or three? I've explained this to many children with success by aiming the hour hand at the two and saying, "He just had his second birthday and is now two." Then I move the hand towards the three a little and ask, "How old is he now? Is he still two?" "Yes." Then I move it a little farther and ask if he's still two. "Yes." I do this until the hand is almost pointing to three and ask the question, "What about the day before his next birthday; how old is he?" "Still two." He is almost three, but still two. Practice this skill until the student can confidently identify which hour it is by moving the hour hand around the clock.

When the hour hand is mastered, put the hours and minutes together. Have the student first identify the hour, and then skip count to find the minutes. Finally, when this is mastered have them tell time without the manipulatives by looking at a clock face.

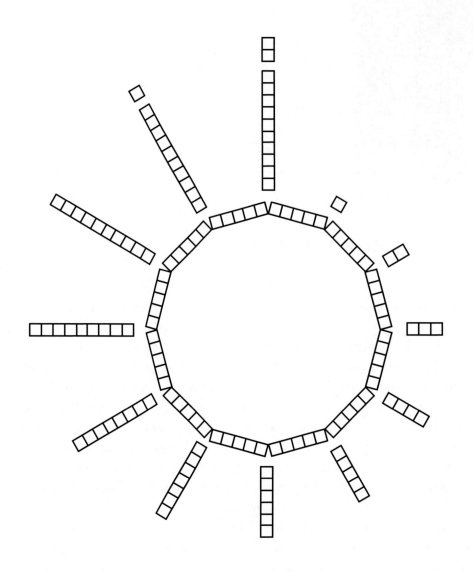

Student Solutions

Lesson Practice 1A

1. colour 3 hundreds, 2 tens, and 4 units; three hundred twenty-four
2. 172; one hundred seventy-two
3. 3 tens and 4 units; thirty-four
4. 2 hundreds, 3 tens, and 5 units; two hundred thirty-five

Lesson Practice 1B

1. colour 6 hundreds, 4 tens and 7 units; six hundred forty-seven
2. 452; four hundred fifty-two
3. 1 ten and 6 units; sixteen
4. 1 hundred, 9 tens, and 8 units; one hundred ninety-eight

Lesson Practice 1C

1. colour 8 hundreds, 1 ten, and 3 units; eight hundred thirteen
2. 125; one hundred twenty-five
3. 6 tens and 7 units; sixty-seven
4. 3 hundreds, 2 tens, and 6 units; three hundred twenty-six

Lesson Practice 1D

1. colour 4 hundreds, 9 tens, and 0 units; four hundred ninety
2. 591; five hundred ninety-one
3. 4 hundreds, 5 tens, and 1 unit; four hundred fifty-one
4. 1 ten and 4 units; fourteen

Lesson Practice 2A

1. 0, 1, 2, 3, 4, 5, 6, 7, 8, 9, 10, 11, 12, 13, 14, 15, 16, 17, 18, 19, 20
2. 0, 1, 2, 3, 4, 5, 6, 7, 8, 9, 10, 11, 12, 13, 14, 15, 16, 17, 18, 19, 20
3. 0, 1, 2, 3, 4, 5, 6, 7, 8, 9, 10, 11, 12, 13, 14, 15, 16, 17, 18, 19, 20
4. 0, 1, 2, 3, 4, 5, 6, 7, 8, 9, 10, 11, 12, 13, 14, 15, 16, 17, 18, 19, 20

Lesson Practice 2B

1. 0, 1, 2, 3, 4, 5, 6, 7, 8, 9, 10, 11, 12, 13, 14, 15, 16, 17, 18, 19, 20
2. 0, 1, 2, 3, 4, 5, 6, 7, 8, 9, 10, 11, 12, 13, 14, 15, 16, 17, 18, 19, 20
3. 0, 1, 2, 3, 4, 5, 6, 7, 8, 9, 10, 11, 12, 13, 14, 15, 16, 17, 18, 19, 20
4. 0, 1, 2, 3, 4, 5, 6, 7, 8, 9, 10, 11, 12, 13, 14, 15, 16, 17, 18, 19, 20

Lesson Practice 2C

1. 0, 1, 2, 3, 4, 5, 6, 7, 8, 9, 10, 11, 12, 13, 14, 15, 16, 17, 18, 19, 20
2. 0, 1, 2, 3, 4, 5, 6, 7, 8, 9, 10, 11, 12, 13, 14, 15, 16, 17, 18, 19, 20
3. 0, 1, 2, 3, 4, 5, 6, 7, 8, 9, 10, 11, 12, 13, 14, 15, 16, 17, 18, 19, 20
4. 0, 1, 2, 3, 4, 5, 6, 7, 8, 9, 10, 11, 12, 13, 14, 15, 16, 17, 18, 19, 20

Systematic Review 2D

1. 0, 1, 2, 3, 4, 5, 6, 7, 8, 9, 10, 11, 12, 13, 14, 15, 16, 17, 18, 19, 20
2. 462; four hundred sixty-two
3. two hundred forty-two
4. seventeen

Systematic Review 2E

1. 0, 1, 2, 3, 4, 5, 6, 7, 8, 9, 10, 11, 12, 13, 14, 15, 16, 17, 18, 19, 20
2. four hundred eighteen
3. fifty-five
4. three hundred seventy-nine

Systematic Review 2F

1. 0, 1, 2, 3, 4, 5, 6, 7, 8, 9, 10, 11, 12, 13, 14, 15, 16, 17, 18, 19, 20
2. 0, 1, 2, 3, 4, 5, 6, 7, 8, 9, 10, 11, 12, 13, 14, 15, 16, 17, 18, 19, 20
3. 146; one hundred forty-six
4. two hundred three
5. eighty-one

Lesson Practice 3A

1. 5 — orange; 3 — pink; 2 — light blue
2. 4 — yellow; 6 — light green; 9 — violet
3. brown 8-block; eight
4. violet 6-block; six
5. tan
6. orange

Lesson Practice 3B

1. 1 — tan; 8 — dark green; 7 — brown
2. 3 — light blue; 9 — pink; 5 — light green
3. dark blue 10-block; ten
4. yellow 4-block; four
5. violet
6. dark green

Lesson Practice 3C

1. 4 — tan; 6 — violet; 7 — yellow
2. 9 — brown; 5 — light blue; 8 — light green
3. orange 2-block; two
4. pink 3-block; three
5. yellow
6. brown

Systematic Review 3D

1. 2 — light blue; 5 — pink; 3 — orange; 1 — green
2. violet 6-block; six
3. light green
4. 203; two hundred three
5. 0, 1, 2, 3, 4, 5, 6, 7, 8, 9, 10, 11, 12, 13, 14, 15, 16, 17, 18, 19, 20

Systematic Review 3E

1. 4 — light green
    8 — yellow
    9 — brown

    (4 → brown, 8 → light green, 9 → yellow)

2. light blue 5-block; five
3. orange
4. 1 hundred, 3 tens, and 5 units;
    one hundred thirty-five
5. 0, 1, 2, 3, 4, 5, 6, 7, 8, 9, 10, 11,
    12, 13, 14, 15, 16, 17, 18, 19, 20

Systematic Review 3F

1. 8 — pink
    6 — light blue
    3 — violet
    5 — brown

    (8 → violet, 6 → brown, 3 → pink, 5 → light blue)

2. yellow 4-block; four
3. pink
4. 3 hundreds, 5 tens, and 7 units;
    three hundred fifty-seven
5. 0, 1, 2, 3, 4, 5, 6, 7, 8, 9, 10, 11,
    12, 13, 14, 15, 16, 17, 18, 19, 20

Lesson Practice 4A

1. $1 + 0 = 1$
2. $3 + 0 = 3$
3. $5 + 0 = 5$
4. $2 + 0 = 2$

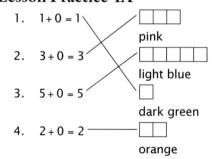

pink
light blue
dark green
orange

5. $7 + 0 = 7$
6. $9 + 0 = 9$
7. $4 + 0 = 4$
8. $6 + 0 = 6$
9. $5 + 0 = 5$
10. $0 + 3 = 3$
11. $0 + 2 = 2$

12. $0 + 0 = 0$
13. done
14. $1 + 0 = 1$ time

Lesson Practice 4B

1. $4 + 0 = 4$
2. $6 + 0 = 6$
3. $3 + 0 = 3$
4. $8 + 0 = 8$

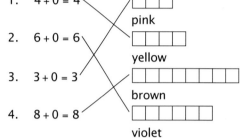

pink
yellow
brown
violet

5. $5 + 0 = 5$
6. $0 + 0 = 0$
7. $7 + 0 = 7$
8. $1 + 0 = 1$
9. $3 + 0 = 3$
10. $0 + 6 = 6$
11. $0 + 9 = 9$
12. $0 + 2 = 2$
13. $4 + 0 = 4$ stories
14. $0 + 8 = 8$ pets

Lesson Practice 4C

1. $9 + 0 = 9$
2. $2 + 0 = 2$
3. $6 + 0 = 6$
4. $5 + 0 = 5$

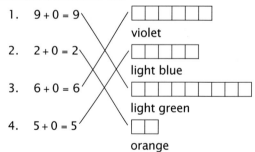

violet
light blue
light green
orange

5. $0 + 1 = 1$
6. $6 + 0 = 6$
7. $9 + 0 = 9$
8. $2 + 0 = 2$
9. $0 + 0 = 0$
10. $0 + 5 = 5$

11. $0 + 7 = 7$

12. $8 + 0 = 8$

13. $7 + 0 = 7$ dollars

14. $0 + 0 = 0$ pictures

11. 0, 1, 2, 3, 4, 5, 6, 7, 8, 9, 10, 11, 12, 13, 14, 15, 16, 17, 18, 19, 20

12. 3 hundreds, 1 ten, and 4 units; three hundred fourteen

13. 4 hundreds, and 2 tens; four hundred twenty

14. brown

15. $0 + 2 = 2$ centimetres

Systematic Review 4D

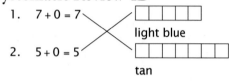

1. $7 + 0 = 7$

light blue

2. $5 + 0 = 5$

tan

3. $1 + 0 = 1$

4. $8 + 0 = 8$

5. $0 + 6 = 6$

6. $0 + 0 = 0$

7. $9 + 0 = 9$

8. $0 + 4 = 4$

9. $0 + 3 = 3$

10. $2 + 0 = 2$

11. 0, 1, 2, 3, 4, 5, 6, 7, 8, 9, 10, 11, 12, 13, 14, 15, 16, 17, 18, 19, 20

12. 1 hundred, 8 tens, and 2 units; one hundred eighty-two

13. 2 hundreds and 9 units

14. tan

15. $3 + 0 = 3$ helpings

Systematic Review 4F

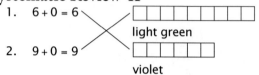

1. $6 + 0 = 6$

light green

2. $9 + 0 = 9$

violet

3. $1 + 0 = 1$

4. $6 + 0 = 6$

5. $0 + 2 = 2$

6. $4 + 0 = 4$

7. $7 + 0 = 7$

8. $0 + 0 = 0$

9. $3 + 0 = 3$

10. $0 + 5 = 5$

11. 0, 1, 2, 3, 4, 5, 6, 7, 8, 9, 10, 11, 12, 13, 14, 15, 16, 17, 18, 19, 20

12. 1 hundred, 4 tens, and 8 units; one hundred forty-eight

13. 3 hundreds, 2 tens, and 5 units three hundred twenty-five

14. light blue

15. $0 + 6 = 6$ cookies

Systematic Review 4E

1. $2 + 0 = 2$

orange

2. $4 + 0 = 4$

yellow

3. $8 + 0 = 8$

4. $5 + 0 = 5$

5. $0 + 0 = 0$

6. $9 + 0 = 9$

7. $1 + 0 = 1$

8. $0 + 6 = 6$

9. $7 + 0 = 7$

10. $0 + 3 = 3$

Lesson Practice 5A

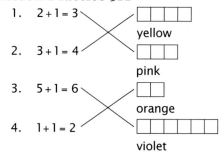

1. $2 + 1 = 3$ — yellow
2. $3 + 1 = 4$ — pink
3. $5 + 1 = 6$ — orange
4. $1 + 1 = 2$ — violet
5. $4 + 1 = 5$
6. $6 + 1 = 7$
7. $8 + 1 = 9$
8. $7 + 1 = 8$
9. $2 + 1 = 3$
10. $1 + 5 = 6$
11. $1 + 3 = 4$
12. $1 + 1 = 2$
13. done
14. $1 + 4 = 5$ flowers

Lesson Practice 5C

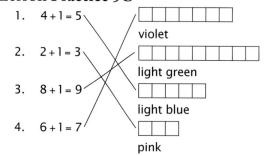

1. $4 + 1 = 5$ — violet
2. $2 + 1 = 3$ — light green
3. $8 + 1 = 9$ — light blue
4. $6 + 1 = 7$ — pink
5. $1 + 0 = 1$
6. $9 + 1 = 10$
7. $1 + 5 = 6$
8. $3 + 1 = 4$
9. $1 + 1 = 2$
10. $1 + 7 = 8$
11. $8 + 1 = 9$
12. $6 + 1 = 7$
13. $2 + 1 = 3$ candy canes
14. $4 + 1 = 5$ tires

Lesson Practice 5B

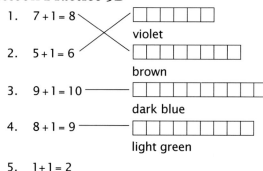

1. $7 + 1 = 8$ — violet
2. $5 + 1 = 6$ — brown
3. $9 + 1 = 10$ — dark blue
4. $8 + 1 = 9$ — light green
5. $1 + 1 = 2$
6. $3 + 1 = 4$
7. $5 + 1 = 6$
8. $2 + 1 = 3$
9. $7 + 1 = 8$
10. $1 + 8 = 9$
11. $1 + 6 = 7$
12. $4 + 1 = 5$
13. $5 + 1 = 6$ CDs
14. $1 + 9 = 10$ pots

Systematic Review 5D

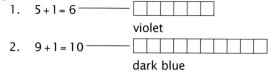

1. $5 + 1 = 6$ — violet
2. $9 + 1 = 10$ — dark blue
3. $2 + 1 = 3$
4. $7 + 0 = 7$
5. $1 + 9 = 10$
6. $7 + 1 = 8$
7. $4 + 0 = 4$
8. $1 + 5 = 6$
9. $6 + 1 = 7$
10. $8 + 0 = 8$
11. $3 + 1 = 4$
12. $1 + 8 = 9$
13. $4 + 1 = 5$
14. $1 + 0 = 1$
15. 315; three hundred fifteen
16. 1 hundred and 5 tens
    one hundred fifty

17. 4 hundreds, 7 tens, and 3 units;
    four hundred seventy-three
18. 3 + 1 = 4 cookies
    4 + 0 = 4 cookies

Systematic Review 5E

1. 3 + 1 = 4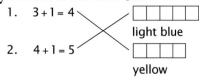
   light blue
2. 4 + 1 = 5
   yellow

3. 1 + 6 = 7
4. 8 + 1 = 9
5. 0 + 4 = 4
6. 1 + 5 = 6
7. 3 + 0 = 3
8. 1 + 7 = 8
9. 9 + 1 = 10
10. 1 + 1 = 2
11. 2 + 1 = 3
12. 8 + 0 = 8
13. 3 + 1 = 4
14. 1 + 4 = 5
15. 172; one hundred seventy-two
16. 3 hundreds and 9 units;
    three hundred nine
17. 8 tens and 5 units;
    eighty-five
18. 7 + 0 = 7 dollars

Systematic Review 5F

1. 6 + 1 = 7 ⬜⬜⬜⬜⬜⬜⬜
   violet
2. 7 + 1 = 8 ⬜⬜⬜⬜⬜⬜⬜⬜
   brown

3. 9 + 1 = 10
4. 3 + 0 = 3
5. 1 + 8 = 9
6. 6 + 1 = 7
7. 1 + 1 = 2
8. 0 + 5 = 5

9. 6 + 0 = 6
10. 4 + 1 = 5
11. 2 + 1 = 3
12. 1 + 5 = 6
13. 3 + 1 = 4
14. 1 + 7 = 8
15. 223; two hundred twenty-three
16. 4 hundreds, 1 ten, and 8 units;
    four hundred eighteen
17. 2 hundreds and 1 unit;
    two hundred one
18. 3 + 1 = 4 centimetres
    4 + 1 = 5 centimetres

Lesson Practice 6A

1.
```
 0  1  2  3  4  5  6  7  8  9
10 11 12 13 14 15 16 17 18 19
20 21 22 23 24 25 26 27 28 29
30 31 32 33 34 35 36 37 38 39
40 41 42 43 44 45 46 47 48 49
50 51 52 53 54 55 56 57 58 59
60 61 62 63 64 65 66 67 68 69
70 71 72 73 74 75 76 77 78 79
80 81 82 83 84 85 86 87 88 89
90 91 92 93 94 95 96 97 98 99
100
```
2. 10, 20, 30, 40, 50, 60

Lesson Practice 6B

1. see grid for 6A – 1
2. 10, 20, 30, 40, 50, 60, 70, 80

Lesson Practice 6C

1. see grid for 6A – 1
2. 10, 20, 30, 40, 50, 60, 70, 80, 90, 100

Systematic Review 6D

1. see grid for 6A – 1
2. 10, 20, 30, 40, 50, 60, 70, 80, 90, 100
3. $1+1=2$
4. $8+0=8$
5. $5+1=6$
6. $7+0=7$

Systematic Review 6E

1. see grid for 6A – 1
2. 10, 20, 30, 40, 50, 60, 70, 80, 90, 100
3. $0+5=5$
4. $6+1=7$
5. $4+1=5$
6. $0+3=3$

Systematic Review 6F

1. see grid for 6A – 1
2. 10, 20, 30, 40, 50, 60, 70, 80, 90, 100
3. $1+2=3$
4. $7+1=8$
5. $9+1=10$
6. $0+4=4$

Lesson Practice 7A

1. green (1) + orange (2) = pink (3)
2. tan (7) + orange (2) = light green (9)
3. pink (3) + orange (2) = light blue (5)
4. orange (2) + orange (2) = yellow (4)
5. $6+2=8$
6. $8+2=10$
7. $50+20=70$
8. $200+200=400$
9. $7+2=9$
10. $4+2=6$
11. $2+3=5$
12. $0+2=2$

13. done
14. $8+2=10$ cars

Lesson Practice 7B

1. light blue (5) + orange (2) = violet (7)
2. yellow (4) + orange (2) = light blue (6)
3. brown (8) + orange (2) = dark blue (10)
4. (0) + orange (2) = orange (2)
5. $2+2=4$
6. $7+2=9$
7. $20+60=80$
8. $100+200=300$
9. $2+5=7$
10. $4+2=6$
11. $2+8=10$
12. $3+2=5$
13. $7+2=9$ sailboats
14. $4+2=6$ crackers

Lesson Practice 7C

1. violet (6) + orange (2) = dark brown (8)
2. green (1) + orange (2) = pink (3)
3. tan (7) + orange (2) = light green (9)
4. pink (3) + orange (2) = light blue (5)
5. $2+8=10$
6. $0+2=2$
7. $40+20=60$
8. $200+100=300$
9. $2+2=4$
10. $2+5=7$
11. $7+2=9$
12. $3+2=5$
13. $5+2=7$ lollipops
14. $3+2=5$ children

Systematic Review 7D
1. brown(8) + orange(2) = dark blue (10)
2. light blue(5) + orange(2) = tan (7)
3. 3 + 2 = 5
4. 2 + 6 = 8
5. 2 + 4 = 6
6. 70 + 20 = 90
7. 300 + 100 = 400
8. 9 + 0 = 9
9. 1 + 2 = 3
10. 1 + 8 = 9
11. 2 + 0 = 2
12. 1 + 6 = 7
13. 9 + 1 = 10
14. 1 + 3 = 4
15. 2 hundreds, 6 tens, and 4 units; two hundred sixty-four
16. 10, 20, 30, 40, 50, 60, 70, 80, 90, 100
17. 2 + 2 = 4 games
18. 6 + 1 = 7 pennies

Systematic Review 7E
1. orange(2) + orange(2) = yellow (4)
2. yellow(4) + orange(2) = violet (6)
3. 2 + 5 = 7
4. 2 + 7 = 9
5. 30 + 20 = 50
6. 200 + 100 = 300
7. 6 + 2 = 8
8. 8 + 1 = 9
9. 8 + 2 = 10
10. 0 + 5 = 5
11. 0 + 6 = 6
12. 1 + 5 = 6
13. 3 + 0 = 3
14. 7 + 1 = 8
15. 4 hundreds and 7 units; four hundred seven
16. 10, 20, 30, 40, 50, 60, 70, 80, 90, 100

17. 8 + 2 = 10 flowers
18. 7 + 2 = 9 points
    9 + 1 = 10 points

Systematic Review 7F
1. pink(3) + orange(2) = light blue (5)
2. violet(6) + orange(2) = dark brown (8)
3. 2 + 4 = 6
4. 7 + 2 = 9
5. 50 + 20 = 70
6. 1 + 2 = 3
7. 2 + 0 = 2
8. 2 + 2 = 4
9. 8 + 2 = 10
10. 100 + 100 = 200
11. 9 + 0 = 9
12. 7 + 0 = 7
13. 9 + 1 = 10
14. 1 + 3 = 4
15. 3 hundreds, 2 tens, and 2 units; three hundred twenty-two
16. 8 tens and 1 unit eighty-one
17. 2 + 4 = 6 dollars
18. 5 + 2 = 7 years old
    7 + 1 = 8 years old

Lesson Practice 8A
1. yellow(4) + orange(2) = violet(6)
2. yellow(4) + 0 = yellow(4)
3. tan(7) + orange(2) = light green(9)
4. dark green(1) + dark green(1) = orange(2)
5. 3 + 2 = 5
6. 5 + 2 = 7
7. 8 + 0 = 8
8. 8 + 1 = 9
9. 6 + 2 = 8
10. 3 + 1 = 4

11. done

12. $\boxed{1} + 2 = 3$ places

Lesson Practice 8B

1. orange(2) + orange(2) = yellow(4)
2. violet(6) + 0 = violet(6)
3. violet(6) + orange(2) = brown(8)
4. light blue(5) + dark green(1) = violet(6)
5. $\boxed{8} + 2 = 10$
6. $\boxed{6} + 1 = 7$
7. $\boxed{9} + 0 = 9$
8. $\boxed{7} + 2 = 9$
9. $\boxed{4} + 1 = 5$
10. $\boxed{0} + 2 = 2$
11. $\boxed{8} + 1 = 9$ children
12. $\boxed{2} + 4 = 6$ items

Lesson Practice 8C

1. light blue(5) + 0 = light blue(5)
2. tan(7) + dark green(1) = dark brown(8)
3. dark brown(8) + dark green(1) = light green(9)
4. light blue(5) + orange(2) = tan(7)
5. $\boxed{1} + 2 = 3$
6. $\boxed{9} + 1 = 10$
7. $\boxed{2} + 0 = 2$
8. $\boxed{4} + 2 = 6$
9. $\boxed{0} + 1 = 1$
10. $\boxed{3} + 1 = 4$
11. $\boxed{3} + 2 = 5$ tractors
12. $\boxed{7} + 2 = 9$ people

Systematic Review 8D

1. $\boxed{0} + 0 = 0$
2. $\boxed{8} + 2 = 10$
3. $\boxed{2} + 2 = 4$
4. $\boxed{6} + 1 = 7$
5. $\boxed{4} + 1 = 5$
6. $\boxed{3} + 2 = 5$
7. $2 + 1 = 3$
8. $40 + 20 = 60$
9. $6 + 0 = 6$
10. $5 + 2 = 7$
11. $3 + 0 = 3$
12. $7 + 1 = 8$
13. $8 + 2 = 10$
14. $1 + 4 = 5$
15. 132;
    one hundred thirty-two
16. 69;
    sixty-nine
17. $2 + 0 = 2$ hands
18. $5 + 2 = 7$ loaves
    $7 + \boxed{2} = 9$ loaves

Systematic Review 8E

1. $\boxed{1} + 2 = 3$
2. $\boxed{3} + 2 = 5$
3. $\boxed{7} + 0 = 7$
4. $\boxed{9} + 1 = 10$
5. $\boxed{6} + 2 = 8$
6. $\boxed{3} + 1 = 4$
7. $1 + 0 = 1$
8. $60 + 10 = 70$
9. $1 + 5 = 6$
10. $7 + 2 = 9$
11. $2 + 2 = 4$
12. $2 + 6 = 8$
13. $4 + 0 = 4$

14. $1+3=4$
15. 124; one hundred twenty-four
16. 76; seventy-six
17. $5+1=6$ children
18. $4+1=5$ hats
    $5+2=7$ hats

Systematic Review 8F

1. $\boxed{0}+2=2$
2. $\boxed{4}+2=6$
3. $\boxed{7}+1=8$
4. $\boxed{5}+1=6$
5. $\boxed{1}+0=1$
6. $\boxed{5}+2=7$
7. $3+2=5$
8. $80+10=90$
9. $1+1=2$
10. $8+0=8$
11. $0+9=9$
12. $2+5=7$
13. $9+1=10$
14. $2+8=10$
15. 201; two hundred one
16. 30; thirty
17. $7+2=9$ tennis balls
18. $\boxed{2}+2=4$ people

Lesson Practice 9A

1. $9+8=$ $10+2=12$
2. $9+1=$ $10+3=13$
3. $9+3=$ $10+7=17$
4. $9+4=$ $10+0=10$
5. $9+9=18$
6. $9+5=14$
7. $9+2=11$
8. $9+3=12$
9. $9+6=15$
10. $1+9=10$

11. $9+4=13$
12. $9+8=17$
13. $9+7=16$ boys
14. $9+9=18$ books

Lesson Practice 9B

1. $9+2=$ ——— $10+1=11$
2. $9+5=$ $10+6=16$
3. $9+7=$ $10+2=12$
4. $9+3=$ $10+4=14$
5. $9+8=17$
6. $9+4=13$
7. $9+7=16$
8. $9+1=10$
9. $5+9=14$
10. $0+9=9$
11. $9+3=12$
12. $9+9=18$
13. $9+6=15$ sets
14. $9+3=12$ CDs

Lesson Practice 9C

1. $9+6=$ $10+8=18$
2. $9+9=$ $10+5=15$
3. $9+4=$ $10+6=16$
4. $9+7=$ $10+3=13$
5. $7+9=16$
6. $9+8=17$
7. $9+2=11$
8. $9+4=13$
9. $6+9=15$
10. $9+3=12$
11. $9+9=18$
12. $9+0=9$
13. $9+5=14$ candies
14. $1+9=10$ dogs

Systematic Review 9D

1. $9 + 9 = 18$
2. $5 + 2 = 7$
3. $40 + 10 = 50$
4. $9 + 7 = 16$
5. $200 + 200 = 400$
6. $5 + 9 = 14$
7. $1 + 6 = 7$
8. $9 + 6 = 15$
9. $9 + 0 = 9$
10. $8 + 9 = 17$
11. $7 + 2 = 9$
12. $9 + 1 = 10$
13. $\boxed{9} + 4 = 13$
14. $\boxed{4} + 2 = 6$
15. 4 hundreds, 6 tens, and 1 unit; four hundred sixty-one
16. 10, 20, 30, 40, 50, 60, 70, 80, 90, 100
17. $8 + 9 = 17$ years old
18. $\boxed{1} + 6 = 7$ guests

Systematic Review 9E

1. $9 + 3 = 12$
2. $4 + 9 = 13$
3. $60 + 20 = 80$
4. $0 + 4 = 4$
5. $2 + 9 = 11$
6. $9 + 9 = 18$
7. $8 + 2 = 10$
8. $300 + 100 = 400$
9. $5 + 9 = 14$
10. $2 + 4 = 6$
11. $9 + 5 = 14$
12. $1 + 7 = 8$
13. $\boxed{9} + 8 = 17$
14. $\boxed{2} + 5 = 7$
15. 2 hundreds, 4 tens, and 9 units; two hundred forty-nine
16. 10, 20, 30, 40, 50, 60, 70, 80, 90, 100

17. $\boxed{3} + 9 = 12$ dollars
18. $4 + 2 = 6$ calls
    $6 + 9 = 15$ calls

Systematic Review 9F

1. $8 + 9 = 17$
2. $9 + 7 = 16$
3. $2 + 2 = 4$
4. $80 + 10 = 90$
5. $0 + 0 = 0$
6. $9 + 3 = 12$
7. $6 + 2 = 8$
8. $10 + 50 = 60$
9. $9 + 4 = 13$
10. $2 + 9 = 11$
11. $2 + 7 = 9$
12. $9 + 5 = 14$
13. $\boxed{6} + 9 = 15$
14. $\boxed{2} + 3 = 5$
15. 5 tens and 2 units; fifty-two
16. 10, 20, 30, 40, 50, 60, 70, 80, 90, 100
17. $\boxed{5} + 2 = 7$ children
18. $5 + 2 = 7$ ducks
    $7 + \boxed{2} = 9$ ducks
    The unknown may be put in either the first or the second blank of the equation.

Lesson Practice 10A

1. $8 + 5 =$ $10 + 1 = 11$
2. $8 + 8 =$ $10 + 3 = 13$
3. $8 + 3 =$ $10 + 4 = 14$
4. $8 + 6 =$ $10 + 6 = 16$
5. $8 + 1 = 9$
6. $8 + 3 = 11$
7. $8 + 7 = 15$
8. $8 + 9 = 17$
9. $8 + 2 = 10$
10. $8 + 4 = 12$
11. $8 + 5 = 13$

12. $8+6=14$
13. $8+2=10$ snowballs
14. $8+4=12$ goldfish

Lesson Practice 10B

1. $8+4=$ $10+0=10$
2. $8+9=$ $10+5=15$
3. $8+7=$ $10+7=17$
4. $8+2=$ $10+2=12$
5. $8+5=13$
6. $8+8=16$
7. $1+8=9$
8. $8+3=11$
9. $6+8=14$
10. $8+7=15$
11. $9+8=17$
12. $8+4=12$
13. $8+8=16$ guests
14. $8+3=11$ beach balls

Lesson Practice 10C

1. $8+1=$ $10+1=11$
2. $8+3=$ 9
3. $8+6=$ $10+6=16$
4. $8+8=$ $10+4=14$
5. $9+8=17$
6. $7+8=15$
7. $8+0=8$
8. $2+8=10$
9. $8+5=13$
10. $6+8=14$
11. $4+8=12$
12. $1+8=9$
13. $8+6=14$
14. $8+0=8$

Systematic Review 10D

1. $8+2=10$
2. $5+8=13$
3. $8+7=15$
4. $8+8=16$
5. $9+5=14$
6. $7+9=16$
7. $20+40=60$
8. $9+8=17$
9. $1+7=8$
10. $5+2=7$
11. $3+0=3$
12. $7+2=9$
13. done
14. $\boxed{4}+8=12$
15. $8+5=13$ cents
16. $9+6=15$ birds
17. $\boxed{2}+7=9$
18. $8+1=9$ apples
    $9+2=11$ apples

Systematic Review 10E

1. $1+8=9$
2. $8+7=15$
3. $8+5=13$
4. $6+8=14$
5. $8+2=10$
6. $9+6=15$
7. $20+30=50$
8. $3+9=12$
9. $6+0=6$
10. $2+2=4$
11. $9+4=13$
12. $6+2=8$
13. $\boxed{3}+8=11$
14. $\boxed{8}+9=17$
15. $4+8=12$ years
16. $9+2=11$ dolls
17. $6+\boxed{8}=14$ leaves
18. $7+2=9$ things
    $9+1=10$ things

Systematic Review 10F

1. $8 + 8 = 16$
2. $3 + 8 = 11$
3. $8 + 6 = 14$
4. $9 + 8 = 17$
5. $9 + 1 = 10$
6. $9 + 3 = 12$
7. $9 + 9 = 18$
8. $100 + 200 = 300$
9. $8 + 7 = 15$
10. $7 + 2 = 9$
11. $9 + 6 = 15$
12. $5 + 9 = 14$
13. $\boxed{9} + 2 = 11$
14. $\boxed{8} + 5 = 13$
15. $9 + \boxed{7} = 16$
16. $6 + 2 = 8$ years old
17. $8 + 8 = 16$ goodies
18. $5 + 2 = 7$ dollars
    $7 + 8 = 15$ dollars

Lesson Practice 11A

1. 6
2. 4
3. 2 circles
   3 triangles
4. 1 circle
   1 triangle
5. 2, 4, 6, 8, 10, 12
6. 2, 4, 6, 8, 10
7. circle
8. triangles

Lesson Practice 11B

1. 5
2. 6
3. 3
4. 7
5. 2, 4, 6, 8, 10, 12, 14
6. 2, 4, 6, 8, 10, 12, 14, 16

7. a triangle
8. a circle

Lesson Practice 11C

1. 4
2. 6
3. 5
4. 3
5. 7
6. 9
7. 3 circles
8. 4 triangles
9. 2, 4, 6, 8, 10, 12, 14, 16, 18, 20

Systematic Review 11D

1. 4 circles
   4 triangles
2. $8 + 3 = 11$
3. $5 + 8 = 13$
4. $8 + 9 = 17$
5. $4 + 8 = 12$
6. $9 + 7 = 16$
7. $9 + 6 = 15$
8. $2 + 3 = 5$
9. $10 + 70 = 80$
10. $4 + 2 = 6$
11. $7 + 8 = 15$
12. $9 + 9 = 18$
13. $6 + 0 = 6$
14. $8 + \boxed{7} = 15$
15. $\boxed{5} + 2 = 7$
16. 2, 4, 6, 8, 10, 12, 14, 16, 18, 20
17. circles
18. $5 + 2 = 7$ kilometres
    $7 + \boxed{2} = 9$ kilometres

Systematic Review 11E

1. 5 circles

    6 triangles
2. $8 + 5 = 13$
3. $9 + 4 = 13$
4. $6 + 1 = 7$
5. $7 + 8 = 15$
6. $8 + 8 = 16$
7. $9 + 5 = 14$
8. $2 + 8 = 10$
9. $70 + 20 = 90$
10. $8 + 0 = 8$
11. $6 + 2 = 8$
12. $8 + 4 = 12$
13. $9 + 8 = 17$
14. $\boxed{8} + 6 = 14$
15. $8 + \boxed{2} = 10$
16. 2, 4, 6, 8, 10, 12, 14, 16, 18, 20
17. a triangle
18. $5 + 1 = 6$ sweaters

    $6 + \boxed{2} = 8$ sweaters

Systematic Review 11F

1. 3 circles

    3 triangles
2. $3 + 8 = 11$
3. $9 + 8 = 17$
4. $9 + 9 = 18$
5. $8 + 2 = 10$
6. $300 + 100 = 400$
7. $7 + 9 = 16$
8. $4 + 0 = 4$
9. $8 + 7 = 15$
10. $9 + 3 = 12$
11. $2 + 9 = 11$
12. $6 + 8 = 14$
13. $8 + 8 = 16$
14. $9 + \boxed{7} = 16$
15. $2 + \boxed{3} = 5$
16. 2, 4, 6, 8, 10, 12, 14, 16, 18, 20

17. 9 sides
18. $6 + 1 = 7$ cars

    $7 + 9 = 16$ cars

Lesson Practice 12A

1. $3 + 3 =$ ⟍ $10 + 4 = 14$
2. $4 + 4 =$ ╳ $3 + 3 = 6$
3. $7 + 7 =$ ⟋ $4 + 4 = 8$
4. five plus five equals ten
5. four plus four equals eight
6. $2 + 2 = 4$
7. $8 + 8 = 16$
8. $3 + 3 = 6$
9. $1 + 1 = 2$
10. $6 + 6 = 12$
11. $9 + 9 = 18$
12. $7 + 7 = 14$ children

Lesson Practice 12B

1. $5 + 5 = 10$ —— $5 + 5 = 10$
2. $8 + 8 = 16$ ⟍ $10 + 2 = 12$
3. $6 + 6 = 12$ ⟋ $10 + 6 = 16$
4. one plus one equals two
5. two plus two equals four
6. $1 + 1 = 2$
7. $9 + 9 = 18$
8. $4 + 4 = 8$
9. $3 + 3 = 6$
10. $2 + 2 = 4$
11. $5 + 5 = 10$
12. $4 + 4 = 8$ years

Lesson Practice 12C

1. $7 + 7 =$ ⟍ $10 + 2 = 12$
2. $6 + 6 =$ ╳ $4 + 4 = 8$
3. $4 + 4 =$ ⟋ $10 + 4 = 14$

4. three plus three equals six
5. five plus five equals ten
6. $8 + 8 = 16$
7. $2 + 2 = 4$
8. $7 + 7 = 14$
9. $4 + 4 = 8$
10. $1 + 1 = 2$
11. $9 + 9 = 18$
12. $6 + 6 = 12$ eggs

Systematic Review 12D
1. $40 + 40 = 80$
2. $7 + 7 = 14$
3. $3 + 3 = 6$
4. $6 + 6 = 12$
5. $8 + 3 = 11$
6. $4 + 8 = 12$
7. $9 + 7 = 16$
8. $6 + 8 = 14$
9. $5 + 5 = 10$
10. $4 + 2 = 6$
11. $9 + 9 = 18$
12. $8 + 1 = 9$
13. $\boxed{8} + 8 = 16$
14. $\boxed{5} + 9 = 14$
15. $\boxed{2} + 5 = 7$
16. 4
17. 3
18. 2, 4, 6, 8, 10, 12, 14, 16, 18, 20
19. $8 + \boxed{7} = 15$ people
20. $3 + 2 = 5$ candles
    $5 + \boxed{1} = 6$ candles

Systematic Review 12E
1. $5 + 5 = 10$
2. $8 + 8 = 16$
3. $7 + 7 = 14$
4. $30 + 30 = 60$
5. $6 + 6 = 12$

6. $8 + 7 = 15$
7. $5 + 8 = 13$
8. $9 + 3 = 12$
9. $3 + 3 = 6$
10. $8 + 2 = 10$
11. $9 + 8 = 17$
12. $2 + 3 = 5$
13. $\boxed{2} + 2 = 4$
14. $\boxed{9} + 6 = 15$
15. $\boxed{1} + 7 = 8$
16. 3 circles
17. 3 triangles
18. 2, 4, 6, 8, 10, 12, 14, 16, 18, 20
19. triangle
20. $9 + \boxed{4} = 13$ pennies

Systematic Review 12F
1. $8 + 8 = 16$
2. $6 + 6 = 12$
3. $200 + 200 = 400$
4. $5 + 5 = 10$
5. $4 + 4 = 8$
6. $7 + 7 = 14$
7. $8 + 6 = 14$
8. $4 + 8 = 12$
9. $8 + 9 = 17$
10. $9 + 5 = 14$
11. $6 + 2 = 8$
12. $7 + 0 = 7$
13. $\boxed{8} + 3 = 11$
14. $\boxed{9} + 9 = 18$
15. $\boxed{3} + 3 = 6$
16. ◯ ◯ ◯ ◯
17. △ △ △
18. 10, 20, 30, 40, 50, 60, 70, 80, 90, 100
19. $8 + 8 = 16$ spider legs
20. $3 + \boxed{2} = 5$ centimetres

Lesson Practice 13A

1. 4
2. 7
3. 3
4. 3
5. 5, 10, 15, 20, 25, 30
6. rectangle
7. 4

Lesson Practice 13B

1. 7
2. 9
3. 4
4. 4
5. 5, 10, 15, 20, 25, 30, 35
6. a square
7. 4

Lesson Practice 13C

1. 6
2. 8
3. 3
4. 3
5. 4
6. 4
7. ☐ ☐
8. ▭ ▭ ▭
9. 5, 10, 15, 20, 25, 30, 35, 40, 45, 50

Systematic Review 13D

1. $6 + 6 = 12$
2. $8 + 8 = 16$
3. $7 + 9 = 16$
4. $8 + 3 = 11$
5. $4 + 4 = 8$
6. $9 + 8 = 17$
7. $50 + 20 = 70$
8. $7 + 7 = 14$
9. $1 + 7 = 8$
10. $5 + 5 = 10$
11. $8 + 6 = 14$
12. $9 + 5 = 14$
13. $\boxed{3} + 3 = 6$
14. $\boxed{8} + 4 = 12$
15. $\boxed{9} + 9 = 18$
16. 4
17. 2
18. 5, 10, 15, 20, 25, 30, 35, 40, 45, 50
19. 8 sides
20. $4 + 1 = 5$ pictures
    $5 + 5 = 10$ pictures

Systematic Review 13E

1. $3 + 3 = 6$
2. $50 + 10 = 60$
3. $9 + 4 = 13$
4. $8 + 7 = 15$
5. $6 + 6 = 12$
6. $4 + 0 = 4$
7. $4 + 4 = 8$
8. $3 + 9 = 12$
9. $7 + 7 = 14$
10. $8 + 5 = 13$
11. $6 + 2 = 8$
12. $9 + 9 = 18$
13. $\boxed{8} + 0 = 8$
14. $\boxed{6} + 6 = 12$
15. $\boxed{9} + 7 = 16$
16. 3 circles
17. 2 rectangles
18. 5, 10, 15, 20, 25, 30, 35, 40, 45, 50
19. $\boxed{3} + 9 = 12$ games
20. $6 + 2 = 8$ pies
    $8 + \boxed{1} = 9$ pies

Systematic Review 13F

1. $9 + 7 = 16$
2. $5 + 5 = 10$
3. $8 + 9 = 17$
4. $7 + 7 = 14$
5. $2 + 4 = 6$
6. $300 + 100 = 400$
7. $9 + 5 = 14$
8. $3 + 8 = 11$
9. $4 + 4 = 8$
10. $8 + 7 = 15$
11. $2 + 6 = 8$
12. $8 + 8 = 16$
13. $\boxed{2} + 1 = 3$
14. $\boxed{2} + 7 = 9$
15. $\boxed{1} + 5 = 6$
16.
17.
18. 5, 10, 15, 20, 25, 30, 35, 40, 45, 50
19. $\boxed{7} + 8 = 15$ dollars
20. $6 + 1 = 7$ pies
    $7 + 7 = 14$ pies

Lesson Practice 14A

1. $3 + 4 = 7$
   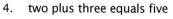
2. $4 + 5 = 9$
3. $6 + 7 = 13$
4. two plus three equals five
5. one plus two equals three
6. $7 + 8 = 15$
7. $1 + 2 = 3$
8. $8 + 9 = 17$
9. $4 + 5 = 9$
10. $2 + 3 = 5$

11. $7 + 8 = 15$

12. $5 + 6 = 11$ pets

Lesson Practice 14B

1. $1 + 2 = 3$

2. $7 + 8 = 15$

3. $2 + 3 = 5$

4. four plus five equals nine

5. three plus four equals seven

6. $5 + 6 = 11$

7. $8 + 9 = 17$

8. $6 + 7 = 13$

9. $7 + 8 = 15$

10. $4 + 3 = 7$

11. $9 + 10 = 19$

12. $6 + 7 = 13$ children

Systematic Review 14D

1. $40 + 50 = 90$

2. $6 + 7 = 13$

3. $8 + 9 = 17$

4. $7 + 8 = 15$

5. $4 + 4 = 8$

6. $8 + 8 = 16$

7. $8 + 6 = 14$

8. $9 + 5 = 14$

9. $5 + 2 = 7$

10. $7 + 1 = 8$

11. $9 + 9 = 18$

12. $2 + 3 = 5$

13. $8 + 3 = 11$

14. $9 + 7 = 16$

15. five plus five equals ten

16. zero plus zero equals zero

17. square

18. triangle

19. $6 + 7 = 13$ squirrels

20. 5, 10, 15, 20, 25, 30, 35, 40, 45, 50

Lesson Practice 14C

1. $5 + 6 = 11$

2. $8 + 9 = 17$

3. $4 + 5 = 9$

4. one plus two equals three

5. two plus three equals five

6. $2 + 3 = 5$

7. $10 + 9 = 19$

8. $6 + 7 = 13$

9. $3 + 4 = 7$

10. $9 + 8 = 17$

11. $6 + 5 = 11$

12. $7 + 8 = 15$ leaves

Systematic Review 14E

1. $30 + 40 = 70$

2. $8 + 7 = 15$

3. $4 + 5 = 9$

4. $8 + 9 = 17$

5. $7 + 7 = 14$

6. $8 + 4 = 12$

7. $9 + 3 = 12$

8. $200 + 700 = 900$

9. $5 + 1 = 6$

10. $6 + 7 = 13$

11. $3 + 3 = 6$

12. $8 + 5 = 13$

13. $9 + 6 = 15$

14. $10 + 2 = 12$

15. three plus two equals five

16. four plus four equals eight

17. rectangle

18. circle

19. 3 + 4 = 7 fingers
20. 2, 4, 6, 8, 10, 12, 14, 16, 18, 20

11. 7 + 3 = 10
12. 6 + 4 = 10 apples

Systematic Review 14F

1. 5 + 6 = 11
2. 50 + 40 = 90
3. 6 + 7 = 13
4. 9 + 8 = 17
5. 2 + 2 = 4
6. 8 + 9 = 17
7. 9 + 4 = 13
8. 600 + 200 = 800
9. 10 + 8 = 18
10. 7 + 1 = 8
11. 9 + 9 = 18
12. 2 + 3 = 5
13. 9 + 7 = 16
14. 4 + 2 = 6
15. six plus one equals seven
16. one plus two equals three
17. rectangle
18. square
19. 8 + 9 = 17 sit-ups
20. 10, 20, 30, 40, 50, 60, 70, 80, 90, 100

Lesson Practice 15A

1. 1 + 9 = 10
2. 6 + 4 = 10
3. 3 + 7 = 10
4. five plus five equals ten
5. eight plus two equals ten
6. 4 + 6 = 10
7. 3 + 7 = 10
8. 5 + 5 = 10
9. 9 + 1 = 10
10. 2 + 8 = 10

Lesson Practice 15B

1. 2 + 8 = 10
2. 5 + 5 = 10
3. 9 + 1 = 10
4. six plus four equals ten
5. seven plus three equals ten
6. 5 + 5 = 10
7. 9 + 1 = 10
8. 6 + 4 = 10
9. 3 + 7 = 10
10. 6 + 4 = 10
11. 5 + 5 = 10
12. 8 + 2 = 10 people

Lesson Practice 15C

1. 7 + 3 = 10
2. 4 + 6 = 10
3. 8 + 2 = 10
4. three plus seven equals ten
5. five plus five equals ten
6. 2 + 8 = 10
7. 7 + 3 = 10
8. 4 + 6 = 10
9. 1 + 9 = 10
10. 4 + 6 = 10
11. 8 + 2 = 10
12. 3 + 7 = 10 runs

Systematic Review 15D

1. $5+5=10$
2. $3+7=10$
3. $6+4=10$
4. $200+300=500$
5. $9+9=18$
6. $8+6=14$
7. $4+8=12$
8. $9+3=12$
9. $7+2=9$
10. $6+7=13$
11. $9+8=17$
12. $2+\boxed{8}=10$
13. $9+\boxed{1}=10$
14. $3+\boxed{4}=7$
15. $4+\boxed{4}=8$
16. $8+\boxed{8}=16$
17. $3+\boxed{7}=10$
18. circles
19. $5+\boxed{5}=10$ years
20. $9+4=13$ models

Systematic Review 15E

1. $8+2=10$
2. $9+1=10$
3. $7+8=15$
4. $4+6=10$
5. $8+9=17$
6. $20+50=70$
7. $9+6=15$
8. $8+3=11$
9. $2+2=4$
10. $5+6=11$
11. $9+7=16$
12. $7+\boxed{3}=10$
13. $4+\boxed{5}=9$
14. $1+\boxed{9}=10$
15. $8+\boxed{8}=16$
16. $6+\boxed{4}=10$
17. $7+\boxed{8}=15$

18. $2+\boxed{8}=10$ years
19. $5+1=6$ balls
    $6+\boxed{4}=10$ balls
20. 5, 10, 15, 20, 25, 30, 35, 40, 45, 50

Systematic Review 15F

1. $7+3=10$
2. $60+20=80$
3. $1+9=10$
4. $8+5=13$
5. $7+7=14$
6. $5+9=14$
7. $9+4=13$
8. $6+6=12$
9. $7+8=15$
10. $3+4=7$
11. $7+1=8$
12. $6+\boxed{0}=6$
13. $3+\boxed{7}=10$
14. $8+\boxed{2}=10$
15. $9+\boxed{5}=14$
16. $8+\boxed{3}=11$
17. $5+\boxed{2}=7$
18. $2+8=10$ times
19. $7+\boxed{3}=10$ years
20. $6+2=8$ chickens
    $8+8=16$ chickens

Lesson Practice 16A

1. $1+8=9$
2. $6+3=9$
3. $7+2=9$
4. nine plus zero equals nine
5. five plus four equals nine
6. $8+1=9$

7. $3 + 6 = 9$
8. $9 + 0 = 9$
9. $2 + 7 = 9$
10. $4 + 5 = 9$
11. $3 + 6 = 9$
12. $7 + \boxed{2} = 9$ books

11. $9 + 0 = 9$
12. $5 + \boxed{4} = 9$ candles

Systematic Review 16D
1. $8 + 1 = 9$
2. $5 + 4 = 9$
3. $60 + 30 = 90$
4. $7 + 2 = 9$
5. $9 + 9 = 18$
6. $7 + 9 = 16$
7. $8 + 4 = 12$
8. $8 + 2 = 10$
9. $3 + 2 = 5$
10. $9 + 6 = 15$
11. $6 + 7 = 13$
12. $7 + \boxed{2} = 9$
13. $8 + \boxed{6} = 14$
14. $7 + \boxed{7} = 14$

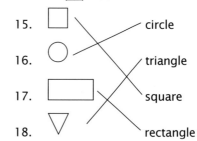

15. □ — circle
16. ○
17. ▭ — square
18. ▽ — rectangle
   triangle
19. 5, 10, 15, 20, 25, 30, 35, 40, 45, 50
20. $3 + 1 = 4$ rooms
   $4 + 2 = 6$ rooms

Lesson Practice 16B
1. $5 + 4 = 9$

2. $8 + 1 = 9$
3. $2 + 7 = 9$
4. three plus six equals nine
5. eight plus one equals nine
6. $6 + 3 = 9$
7. $2 + 7 = 9$
8. $1 + 8 = 9$
9. $0 + 9 = 9$
10. $5 + 4 = 9$
11. $7 + 2 = 9$
12. $6 + \boxed{3} = 9$ cars

Lesson Practice 16C
1. $3 + 6 = 9$
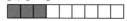
2. $4 + 5 = 9$

3. $9 + 0 = 9$
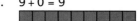
4. one plus eight equals nine
5. four plus five equals nine
6. $7 + 2 = 9$
7. $8 + 1 = 9$
8. $3 + 6 = 9$
9. $5 + 4 = 9$
10. $2 + 7 = 9$

Systematic Review 16E
1. $6 + 6 = 12$
2. $1 + 9 = 10$
3. $50 + 40 = 90$
4. $8 + 3 = 11$
5. $9 + 6 = 15$
6. $5 + 5 = 10$
7. $5 + 6 = 11$
8. $8 + 7 = 15$

9. $5 + 2 = 7$
10. $9 + 0 = 9$
11. $3 + 1 = 4$
12. $7 + \boxed{3} = 10$
13. $2 + \boxed{7} = 9$
14. $9 + \boxed{9} = 18$
15. $3 + 3 = 6$ circles
16. $4 + 1 = 5$ squares
17. $2 + 2 = 4$ triangles
18. $5 + 0 = 5$ rectangles
19. $4 + \boxed{5} = 9$ players
20. $3 + 4 = 7$ flowers
    $7 + \boxed{2} = 9$ flowers

Systematic Review 16F

1. $7 + 3 = 10$
2. $40 + 40 = 80$
3. $9 + 1 = 10$
4. $6 + 3 = 9$
5. $9 + 5 = 14$
6. $8 + 5 = 13$
7. $3 + 2 = 5$
8. $500 + 400 = 900$
9. $5 + 6 = 11$
10. $8 + 7 = 15$
11. $9 + 8 = 17$
12. $6 + \boxed{4} = 10$
13. $5 + \boxed{8} = 13$
14. $6 + \boxed{6} = 12$
15. $4 + 2 = 6$
16. $5 + 4 = 9$
17. $3 + 1 = 4$
18. $2 + 6 = 8$
19. $8 + 0 = 8$ fireflies
20. $6 + 1 = 7$ stories
    $7 + 3 = 10$ stories

Lesson Practice 17A

1. $4 + 7 = 11$

2. $5 + 7 = 12$
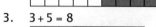
3. $3 + 5 = 8$
4. five plus three equals eight
5. seven plus four equals eleven
6. $4 + 7 = 11$
7. $5 + 7 = 12$
8. $3 + 5 = 8$
9. $7 + 5 = 12$
10. $5 + 3 = 8$
11. $7 + 4 = 11$
12. $5 + 7 = 12$ students

Lesson Practice 17B

1. $5 + 3 = 8$
2. $7 + 5 = 12$
3. $7 + 4 = 11$
4. five plus $\boxed{\text{seven}}$ equals twelve
5. three plus five equals eight
6. $5 + 3 = 8$
7. $7 + 5 = 12$
8. $7 + 4 = 11$
9. $3 + 5 = 8$
10. $4 + 7 = 11$
11. $5 + 7 = 12$
12. $3 + 5 = 8$ baskets

Lesson Practice 17C

1. $7 + 4 = 11$

2. $3 + 5 = 8$
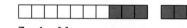
3. $5 + 7 = 12$

4. four plus ⸤seven⸥ equals eleven

5. seven plus ⸤five⸥ equals twelve

6. $3 + 5 = 8$

7. $4 + 7 = 11$

8. $7 + 5 = 12$

9. $7 + 4 = 11$

10. $5 + 7 = 12$

11. $5 + 3 = 8$

12. $4 + 7 = 11$ pictures

Systematic Review 17D

1. $5 + 7 = 12$
2. $50 + 30 = 80$
3. $8 + 6 = 14$
4. $7 + 4 = 11$
5. $7 + 3 = 10$
6. $4 + 5 = 9$
7. $4 + 7 = 11$
8. $300 + 500 = 800$
9. $8 + 2 = 10$
10. $7 + 5 = 12$
11. $6 + 4 = 10$
12. $5 + \boxed{3} = 8$
13. $3 + \boxed{4} = 7$
14. $7 + \boxed{4} = 11$
15. $6 + \boxed{5} = 11$
16. $6 + \boxed{3} = 9$
17. $4 + \boxed{4} = 8$
18. 2, 4, 6, 8, 10, 12, 14, 16, 18, 20
19. $5 + 7 = 12$ creatures
20. $4 + 2 = 6$ shirts
    $6 + 4 = 10$ shirts

Systematic Review 17E

1. $60 + 30 = 90$
2. $7 + 4 = 11$
3. $9 + 3 = 12$
4. $6 + 4 = 10$
5. $7 + 7 = 14$
6. $7 + 5 = 12$

7. $400 + 200 = 600$
8. $4 + 7 = 11$
9. $5 + 3 = 8$
10. $9 + 1 = 10$
11. $2 + 7 = 9$
12. $8 + \boxed{9} = 17$
13. $1 + \boxed{7} = 8$
14. $8 + \boxed{2} = 10$
15. $9 + \boxed{7} = 16$
16. $5 + \boxed{6} = 11$
17. $5 + \boxed{4} = 9$
18. 5, 10, 15, 20, 25, 30, 35, 40, 45, 50
19. $3 + 5 = 8$ kilograms
20. $3 + 1 = 4$ chickens
    $4 + 7 = 11$ chickens

Systematic Review 17F

1. $7 + 3 = 10$
2. $300 + 600 = 900$
3. $8 + 4 = 12$
4. $4 + 7 = 11$
5. $5 + 0 = 5$
6. $4 + 6 = 10$
7. $5 + 7 = 12$
8. $9 + 9 = 18$
9. $5 + 4 = 9$
10. $4 + 0 = 4$
11. $4 + 3 = 7$
12. $9 + \boxed{9} = 18$
13. $5 + \boxed{7} = 12$
14. $5 + \boxed{5} = 10$
15. $3 + \boxed{7} = 10$
16. $3 + \boxed{5} = 8$
17. $7 + \boxed{6} = 13$
18. 10, 20, 30, 40, 50, 60, 70, 80, 90, 100
19. $1 + 2 = 3$ goldfish
    $3 + 6 = 9$ goldfish
20. $4 + 7 = 11$ shapes

Lesson Practice 18A

1. have 5 (blue)
2. owe 3 (pink)
3. have 7 (tan)
4. owe 6 (violet)
5. owe 1 (green)
6. have 2 (orange)
7. $8 - 3 = 5$
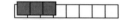
8. $7 - 4 = 3$

9. $9 - 3 = 6$
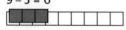
10. $6 - 2 = 4$

11. done
12. $6 - 3 = 3$
13. $8 - 2 = 6$
14. $5 - 4 = 1$

Lesson Practice 18C

1. have 8 (brown)
2. owe 9 (light green)
3. have 2 (orange)
4. owe 6 (violet)
5. owe 5 (light blue)
6. have 7 (tan)
7. $7 - 3 = 4$
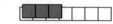
8. $5 - 4 = 1$

9. $6 - 1 = 5$
10. $8 - 7 = 1$
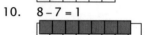
11. $9 - 5 = 4$
12. $4 - 2 = 2$
13. $7 - 6 = 1$
14. $3 - 2 = 1$

Lesson Practice 18B

1. have 3 (pink)
2. owe 5 (light blue)
3. owe 7 (tan)
4. have 4 (yellow)
5. owe 3 (pink)
6. have 1 (green)
7. $9 - 2 = 7$

8. $6 - 5 = 1$
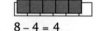
9. $8 - 4 = 4$
10. $3 - 1 = 2$

11. $4 - 3 = 1$
12. $5 - 1 = 4$
13. $9 - 7 = 2$
14. $6 - 4 = 2$

Systematic Review 18D

1. owe 3 (pink)
2. owe 5 (light blue)
3. have 6 (violet)
4. owe 2 (orange)
5. $2 - 1 = 1$
6. $4 - 2 = 2$
7. $5 + 3 = 8$
8. $4 + 7 = 11$
9. $30 + 40 = 70$
10. $8 + 9 = 17$
11. $6 + 6 = 12$
12. $7 + 5 = 12$
13. $6 + 3 = 9$
14. $500 + 400 = 900$
15. $\boxed{8} + 0 = 8$
16. $\boxed{5} + 1 = 6$
17. $\boxed{9} + 0 = 9$
18. $\boxed{5} + 2 = 7$

19. $\boxed{2}+8=10$
20. $3+2=5$ flowers

Systematic Review 18E
1. owe 4 (yellow)
2. have 8 (brown)
3. have 3 (pink)
4. owe 9 (light green)
5. $6-3=3$
6. $7-5=2$
7. $7+6=13$
8. $40+40=80$
9. $6+5=11$
10. $300+500=800$
11. $5+7=12$
12. $7+4=11$
13. $4+5=9$
14. $5+6=11$
15. $\boxed{3}+2=5$
16. $\boxed{3}+1=4$
17. $\boxed{6}+2=8$
18. $\boxed{4}+0=4$
19. $\boxed{3}+7=10$
20. $5+6=11$ books

Systematic Review 18F
1. have 7 (tan)
2. owe 6 (violet)
3. owe 10 (dark blue)
4. have 5 (light blue)
5. $8-5=3$
6. $5-2=3$
7. $4+7=11$
8. $30+50=80$
9. $5+7=12$
10. $9+9=18$
11. $7+5=12$
12. $6+8=14$

13. $7+4=11$
14. $9+6=15$
15. $\boxed{6}+1=7$
16. $\boxed{6}+2=8$
17. $\boxed{8}+1=9$
18. $\boxed{5}+0=5$
19. $\boxed{4}+5=9$
20. $9+6=15$ centimetres

Lesson Practice 19A
1. 10, 9, 8, 7, 6, 5, 4, 3, 2, 1, 0
2. done
3. $5-5=0$
4. $1-0=1$
5. $8-8=0$
6. $6-5=1$
7. $4-1=3$
8. $9-1=8$
9. $7-0=7$
10. $4-3=1$
11. $2-1=1$
12. $10-1=9$
13. $6-6=0$
14. $9-8=1$
15. $5-4=1$
16. eight minus one equals seven
17. $2-0=2$ kittens
18. $5-4=1$ cookie

Lesson Practice 19B
1. 10, 9, 8, 7, 6, 5, 4, 3, 2, 1, 0
2. $5-4=1$
3. $3-3=0$
4. $0-0=0$
5. $3-3=0$
6. $6-1=5$
7. $7-6=1$
8. $10-9=1$
9. $6-0=6$

10. $3 - 1 = 2$
11. $7 - 7 = 0$
12. $4 - 0 = 4$
13. $8 - 7 = 1$
14. $7 - 1 = 6$
15. $1 - 1 = 0$
16. nine minus zero equals nine
17. $9 - 0 = 9$ pennies
18. $9 - 1 = 8$ dollars

Lesson Practice 19C

1. 10, 9, 8, 7, 6, 5, 4, 3, 2, 1, 0
2. $4 - 4 = 0$
3. $6 - 5 = 1$
4. $3 - 0 = 3$
5. $3 - 2 = 1$
6. $5 - 5 = 0$
7. $5 - 0 = 5$
8. $8 - 1 = 7$
9. $5 - 4 = 1$
10. $5 - 1 = 4$
11. $2 - 2 = 0$
12. $8 - 0 = 8$
13. $4 - 1 = 3$
14. $4 - 3 = 1$
15. $8 - 8 = 0$
16. nine minus one equals eight
17. $7 - 6 = 1$ year
18. $9 - 9 = 0$ pennies

Systematic Review 19D

1. $9 - 0 = 9$
2. $1 - 1 = 0$
3. $2 - 1 = 1$
4. $6 - 6 = 0$
5. $3 - 1 = 2$
6. $8 - 7 = 1$
7. $10 - 1 = 9$
8. $7 - 7 = 0$
9. $3 + 9 = 12$

10. $9 + 8 = 17$
11. $6 + 9 = 15$
12. $9 + 5 = 14$
13. $\boxed{7} + 1 = 8$
14. $\boxed{4} + 2 = 6$
15. $\boxed{4} + 0 = 4$
16. $\boxed{3} + 2 = 5$
17. ten minus nine equals one
18. six minus zero equals six
19. $6 - 1 = 5$ cards
20. $3 - 3 = 0$ toys

Systematic Review 19E

1. $3 - 3 = 0$
2. $7 - 1 = 6$
3. $7 - 6 = 1$
4. $4 - 0 = 4$
5. $1 - 1 = 0$
6. $6 - 1 = 5$
7. $9 - 8 = 1$
8. $7 - 0 = 7$
9. $9 + 1 = 10$
10. $9 + 7 = 16$
11. $2 + 9 = 11$
12. $4 + 9 = 13$
13. $\boxed{2} + 2 = 4$
14. $\boxed{7} + 2 = 9$
15. $\boxed{5} + 2 = 7$
16. $\boxed{1} + 2 = 3$
17. four minus three equals one
18. five minus one equals four
19. $6 - 5 = 1$ piece
20. $8 - 0 = 8$ friends

Systematic Review 19F

1. $5 - 4 = 1$
2. $4 - 1 = 3$
3. $8 - 8 = 0$
4. $5 - 0 = 5$

5. $3 - 2 = 1$
6. $8 - 1 = 7$
7. $4 - 4 = 0$
8. $1 - 0 = 1$
9. $9 + 0 = 9$
10. $9 + 9 = 18$
11. $5 + 9 = 14$
12. $8 + 9 = 17$
13. $\boxed{3} + 2 = 5$
14. $\boxed{6} + 2 = 8$
15. $\boxed{0} + 2 = 2$
16. $\boxed{4} + 2 = 6$
17. eight minus seven equals one
18. three minus one equals two
19. $7 - 7 = 0$ friends
20. $10 - 1 = 9$ years

Lesson Practice 20A

1. $5 - 2 = 3$
2. $5 - 3 = 2$
3. $7 - 2 = 5$
4. $7 - 5 = 2$
5. $10 - 2 = 8$
6. $10 - 8 - 2$
7. $30 - 20 = 10$
8. $300 - 100 = 200$
9. $8 - 2 = 6$
10. $8 - 6 = 2$
11. $4 - 2 = 2$
12. $2 - 2 = 0$
13. $11 - 2 = 9$
14. $11 - 9 = 2$
15. $7 - 5 = 2$ years
16. $9 - 2 = 7$ points

Lesson Practice 20B

1. $6 - 2 = 4$
2. $6 - 4 = 2$
3. $9 - 2 = 7$

4. $9 - 7 = 2$
5. $50 - 20 = 30$
6. $5 - 3 = 2$
7. $11 - 2 = 9$
8. $11 - 9 = 2$
9. $400 - 200 = 200$
10. $2 - 2 = 0$
11. $3 - 2 = 1$
12. $2 - 0 = 2$
13. $8 - 6 = 2$
14. $8 - 2 = 6$
15. $10 - 8 = 2$ stickers
16. $10 - 2 = 8$ dollars

Lesson Practice 20C

1. $4 - 2 = 2$
2. $3 - 1 = 2$
3. $10 - 8 = 2$
4. $10 - 2 = 8$
5. $7 - 5 = 2$
6. $70 - 20 - 50$
7. $6 - 2 = 4$
8. $6 - 4 = 2$
9. $8 - 6 = 2$
10. $800 - 200 = 600$
11. $5 - 2 = 3$
12. $5 - 3 = 2$
13. $2 - 2 = 0$
14. $3 - 2 = 1$
15. $9 - 7 = 2$ years
16. $6 - 2 = 4$ fish

Systematic Review 20D

1. $9 - 2 = 7$
2. $7 - 5 = 2$
3. $50 - 10 = 40$
4. $3 - 0 = 3$
5. $8 - 6 = 2$
6. $5 - 2 = 3$
7. $6 - 5 = 1$

8. $7 - 1 = 6$
9. $3 + 8 = 11$
10. $5 + 8 = 13$
11. $8 + 7 = 15$
12. $8 + 2 = 10$
13. $\boxed{9} + 9 = 18$
14. $\boxed{6} + 9 = 15$
15. $\boxed{2} + 9 = 11$
16. $\boxed{4} + 9 = 13$
17. $7 - 2 = 5$ pencils
18. $6 - 4 = 2$ people
19. $8 + 1 = 9$ candy canes
20. $8 + 9 = 17$ candy canes

Systematic Review 20E

1. $400 - 200 = 200$
2. $9 - 7 = 2$
3. $10 - 2 = 8$
4. $11 - 9 = 2$
5. $6 - 6 = 0$
6. $10 - 9 = 1$
7. $9 - 1 = 8$
8. $2 - 0 = 2$
9. $4 + 8 = 12$
10. $8 + 6 = 14$
11. $8 + 3 = 11$
12. $7 + 8 = 15$
13. $\boxed{3} + 9 = 12$
14. $\boxed{5} + 9 = 14$
15. $\boxed{8} + 9 = 17$
16. $\boxed{1} + 9 = 10$
17. $3 - 2 = 1$ more boy
18. $10 - 8 = 2$ people
19. $3 + 2 = 5$ goats
20. $8 + 9 = 17$ pages

Systematic Review 20F

1. $4 - 2 = 2$
2. $7 - 2 = 5$
3. $30 - 10 = 20$
4. $5 - 3 = 2$
5. $7 - 6 = 1$
6. $2 - 2 = 0$
7. $4 - 1 = 3$
8. $9 - 8 = 1$
9. $8 + 9 = 17$
10. $8 + 0 = 8$
11. $8 + 5 = 13$
12. $8 + 8 = 16$
13. $\boxed{7} + 9 = 16$
14. $\boxed{9} + 9 = 18$
15. $\boxed{4} + 9 = 13$
16. $\boxed{6} + 9 = 15$
17. $8 - 2 = 6$ birds
18. $11 - 2 = 9$ years
19. $7 + 4 = 11$ days
20. $5 + 3 = 8$ kilograms

Lesson Practice 21A

1. $18 - 9 = 9$
2. $9 - 9 = 0$
3. $16 - 9 = 7$
4. $15 - 9 = 6$
5. $10 - 9 = 1$
6. $12 - 9 = 3$
7. $17 - 9 = 8$
8. $11 - 9 = 2$
9. $13 - 9 = 4$
10. $18 - 9 = 9$
11. $14 - 9 = 5$
12. $9 - 9 = 0$
13. $17 - 9 = 8$ dollars
14. $12 - 9 = 3$ cars
15. $13 - 9 = 4$ eggs
16. $11 - 9 = 2$ people

Lesson Practice 21B

1. $14 - 9 = 5$
2. $10 - 9 = 1$
3. $15 - 9 = 6$
4. $11 - 9 = 2$
5. $17 - 9 = 8$
6. $13 - 9 = 4$
7. $16 - 9 = 7$
8. $9 - 9 = 0$
9. $12 - 9 = 3$
10. $10 - 9 = 1$
11. $18 - 9 = 9$
12. $14 - 9 = 5$
13. $16 - 9 = 7$ melons
14. $18 - 9 = 9$ days
15. $15 - 9 = 6$ dollars
16. $17 - 9 = 8$ centimetres

Lesson Practice 21C

1. $9 - 9 = 0$
2. $14 - 9 = 5$
3. $11 - 9 = 2$
4. $13 - 9 = 4$
5. $16 - 9 = 7$
6. $10 - 9 = 1$
7. $12 - 9 = 3$
8. $15 - 9 = 6$
9. $18 - 9 = 9$
10. $9 - 9 = 0$
11. $17 - 9 = 8$
12. $11 - 9 = 2$
13. $10 - 9 = 1$ lollipop
14. $12 - 9 = 3$ eggs
15. $16 - 9 = 7$ dollars
16. $13 - 9 = 4$ years

Systematic Review 21D

1. $15 - 9 = 6$
2. $18 - 9 = 9$

3. $11 - 9 = 2$
4. $14 - 9 = 5$
5. $6 - 2 = 4$
6. $7 - 0 = 7$
7. $5 - 5 = 0$
8. $8 - 6 = 2$
9. $40 + 40 = 80$
10. $8 + 8 = 16$
11. $7 + 7 = 14$
12. $3 + 3 = 6$
13. $\boxed{5} + 8 = 13$
14. $\boxed{1} + 8 = 9$
15. $\boxed{7} + 8 = 15$
16. $\boxed{3} + 8 = 11$
17. $17 - 9 = 8$ minutes
18. $9 - 2 = 7$ granola bars
19. $5 + 7 = 12$ children
20. $5 + 3 = 8$ gifts
    $8 - 6 = 2$ gifts

Systematic Review 21E

1. $16 - 9 = 7$
2. $13 - 9 = 4$
3. $9 - 9 = 0$
4. $12 - 9 = 3$
5. $7 - 5 = 2$
6. $40 - 20 = 20$
7. $9 - 2 = 7$
8. $8 - 1 = 7$
9. $5 + 5 = 10$
10. $9 + 9 = 18$
11. $6 + 6 = 12$
12. $200 + 200 = 400$
13. $\boxed{2} + 8 = 10$
14. $\boxed{9} + 8 = 17$
15. $\boxed{4} + 8 = 12$
16. $\boxed{6} + 8 = 14$
17. $10 - 9 = 1$ bird
18. $14 - 9 = 5$ dollars

19. $4 + 5 = 9$ years
20. $6 + 4 = 10$ dollars
    $10 - 1 = 9$ dollars

12. $17 - 8 = 9$
13. $11 - 8 = 3$ bananas
14. $13 - 8 = 5$ books
15. $14 - 8 = 6$ outfits
16. $16 - 8 = 8$ dollars

Systematic Review 21F

1. $17 - 9 = 8$
2. $15 - 9 = 6$
3. $18 - 9 = 9$
4. $11 - 9 = 2$
5. $5 - 3 = 2$
6. $8 - 2 = 6$
7. $7 - 7 = 0$
8. $30 - 10 = 20$
9. $7 + 7 = 14$
10. $4 + 4 = 8$
11. $30 + 30 = 60$
12. $9 + 9 = 18$
13. $\boxed{8} + 8 = 16$
14. $\boxed{8} + 5 = 13$
15. $\boxed{8} + 0 = 8$
16. $\boxed{7} + 8 = 15$
17. $12 - 9 = 3$ questions
18. $8 - 6 = 2$ presents
19. $5 + 3 = 8$ children
    $8 - 2 = 6$ children
20. $7 + 3 = 10$ books

Lesson Practice 22A

1. $16 - 8 = 8$
2. $12 - 8 = 4$
3. $8 - 8 = 0$
4. $10 - 8 = 2$
5. $17 - 8 = 9$
6. $13 - 8 = 5$
7. $11 - 8 = 3$
8. $15 - 8 = 7$
9. $9 - 8 = 1$
10. $14 - 8 = 6$
11. $12 - 8 = 4$

Lesson Practice 22B

1. $10 - 8 = 2$
2. $16 - 8 = 8$
3. $9 - 8 = 1$
4. $15 - 8 = 7$
5. $8 - 8 = 0$
6. $12 - 8 = 4$
7. $14 - 8 = 6$
8. $17 - 8 = 9$
9. $11 - 8 = 3$
10. $13 - 8 = 5$
11. $10 - 8 = 2$
12. $16 - 8 = 8$
13. $9 - 8 = 1$ puppy
14. $10 - 8 = 2$ letters
15. $17 - 8 = 9$ stickers
16. $12 - 8 = 4$ gummi bears

Lesson Practice 22C

1. $13 - 8 = 5$
2. $11 - 8 = 3$
3. $15 - 8 = 7$
4. $8 - 8 = 0$
5. $16 - 8 = 8$
6. $14 - 8 = 6$
7. $12 - 8 = 4$
8. $9 - 8 = 1$
9. $17 - 8 = 9$
10. $10 - 8 = 2$
11. $16 - 8 = 8$
12. $11 - 8 = 3$
13. $8 - 8 = 0$ snowmen
14. $15 - 8 = 7$ days

15. $13 - 8 = 5$ melons
16. $16 - 8 = 8$ kilograms

Systematic Review 22D

1. $14 - 8 = 6$
2. $10 - 8 = 2$
3. $13 - 8 = 5$
4. $15 - 8 = 7$
5. $12 - 9 = 3$
6. $14 - 9 = 5$
7. $70 - 20 = 50$
8. $6 - 4 = 2$
9. $6 + 4 = 10$
10. $9 + 1 = 10$
11. $8 + 2 = 10$
12. $3 + 7 = 10$
13. $\boxed{4} + 4 = 8$
14. $\boxed{5} + 5 = 10$
15. $\boxed{8} + 8 = 16$
16. $\boxed{2} + 2 = 4$
17. $17 - 8 = 9$ grandsons
18. $12 - 8 = 4$ eggs
19. $4 + 3 = 7$ sandwiches
    $7 - 1 = 6$ sandwiches
20. $4 + 5 = 9$ pencils
    $9 - 2 = 7$ pencils

Systematic Review 22E

1. $9 - 8 = 1$
2. $16 - 8 = 8$
3. $11 - 8 = 3$
4. $12 - 8 = 4$
5. $16 - 9 = 7$
6. $10 - 2 = 8$
7. $9 - 7 = 2$
8. $90 - 10 = 80$
9. $1 + 9 = 10$
10. $4 + 6 = 10$
11. $7 + 3 = 10$

12. $2 + 8 = 10$
13. $\boxed{6} + 6 = 12$
14. $\boxed{3} + 3 = 6$
15. $\boxed{7} + 7 = 14$
16. $\boxed{9} + 9 = 18$
17. $15 - 8 = 7$ minutes
18. $4 - 3 = 1$ books
19. $6 + 3 = 9$ runs
20. $10 - 8 = 2$ pennies
    $2 + 7 = 9$ pennies

Systematic Review 22F

1. $17 - 8 = 9$
2. $14 - 8 = 6$
3. $10 - 8 = 2$
4. $13 - 8 = 5$
5. $13 - 9 = 4$
6. $15 - 9 = 6$
7. $5 - 2 = 3$
8. $6 - 0 = 6$
9. $5 + 4 = 9$
10. $3 + 6 = 9$
11. $8 + 1 = 9$
12. $200 + 700 = 900$
13. $\boxed{1} + 1 = 2$
14. $\boxed{4} + 4 = 8$
15. $\boxed{8} + 8 = 16$
16. $\boxed{5} + 5 = 10$
17. $11 - 8 = 3$ marbles
18. $6 + 6 = 12$ chapters
19. $7 + 3 = 10$ years
20. $1 + 1 = 2$ lawns
    $2 + 3 = 5$ lawns

Lesson Practice 23A

1. $14 - 7 = 7$
2. $10 - 5 = 5$
3. $12 - 6 = 6$
4. $60 - 30 = 30$

5. $8 - 4 = 4$
6. $16 - 8 = 8$
7. $10 - 5 = 5$
8. $14 - 7 = 7$
9. $18 - 9 = 9$
10. $4 - 2 = 2$
11. $12 - 6 = 6$
12. $8 - 4 = 4$
13. $2 - 1 = 1$
14. $16 - 8 = 8$
15. $6 - 3 = 3$
16. $14 - 7 = 7$
17. $12 - 6 = 6$ years
18. $16 - 8 = 8$ apples

5. $6 - 3 = 3$
6. $20 - 10 = 10$
7. $18 - 9 = 9$
8. $12 - 6 = 6$
9. $14 - 7 = 7$
10. $8 - 4 = 4$
11. $10 - 5 = 5$
12. $6 - 3 = 3$
13. $18 - 9 = 9$
14. $12 - 6 = 6$
15. $4 - 2 = 2$
16. $16 - 8 = 8$
17. $14 - 7 = 7$ kilometres
18. $4 - 2 = 2$ more sisters

Lesson Practice 23B
1. $60 - 30 = 30$
2. $6 - 3 = 3$
3. $14 - 7 = 7$
4. $12 - 6 = 6$
5. $10 - 5 = 5$
6. $18 - 9 = 9$
7. $400 - 200 = 200$
8. $16 - 8 = 8$
9. $8 - 4 = 4$
10. $10 - 5 = 5$
11. $6 - 3 = 3$
12. $14 - 7 = 7$
13. $12 - 6 = 6$
14. $4 - 2 = 2$
15. $16 - 8 = 8$
16. $18 - 9 = 9$
17. $6 - 3 = 3$ toys
18. $10 - 5 = 5$ hours

Systematic Review 23D
1. $12 - 6 = 6$
2. $13 - 8 = 5$
3. $8 - 4 = 4$
4. $17 - 9 = 8$
5. $14 - 7 = 7$
6. $6 - 5 = 1$
7. $10 - 5 = 5$
8. $11 - 8 = 3$
9. $6 - 3 = 3$
10. $15 - 9 = 6$
11. $9 - 1 = 8$
12. $7 + 4 = 11$
13. $500 + 300 = 800$
14. $7 + 7 = 14$
15. $2 + 8 = 10$
16. $\boxed{6} + 4 = 10$
17. $\boxed{7} + 3 = 10$
18. $\boxed{1} + 9 = 10$
19. $16 - 8 = 8$ dollars
20. $7 + 2 = 9$ turtles
    $9 - 1 = 8$ turtles

Lesson Practice 23C
1. $10 - 5 = 5$
2. $8 - 4 = 4$
3. $16 - 8 = 8$
4. $14 - 7 = 7$

Systematic Review 23E

1. $6 - 3 = 3$
2. $15 - 8 = 7$
3. $10 - 5 = 5$
4. $13 - 9 = 4$
5. $12 - 6 = 6$
6. $5 - 1 = 4$
7. $80 - 40 = 40$
8. $8 - 6 = 2$
9. $14 - 7 = 7$
10. $9 - 2 = 7$
11. $5 - 3 = 2$
12. $6 + 3 = 9$
13. $50 + 40 = 90$
14. $9 + 9 = 18$
15. $7 + 2 = 9$
16. $\boxed{2} + 8 = 10$
17. $\boxed{4} + 6 = 10$
18. $\boxed{3} + 7 = 10$
19. $12 - 6 = 6$ questions
20. $9 + 7 = 16$ children

Systematic Review 23F

1. $18 - 9 = 9$
2. $14 - 8 = 6$
3. $12 - 6 = 6$
4. $12 - 9 = 3$
5. $8 - 4 = 4$
6. $6 - 2 = 4$
7. $600 - 300 = 300$
8. $30 - 10 = 20$
9. $10 - 5 = 5$
10. $14 - 7 = 7$
11. $16 - 9 = 7$
12. $7 + 3 = 10$
13. $1 + 9 = 10$
14. $4 + 5 = 9$
15. $8 + 3 = 11$
16. $\boxed{9} + 1 = 10$
17. $\boxed{5} + 5 = 10$
18. $\boxed{8} + 2 = 10$

19. $9 - 9 = 0$ plates
20. $8 + 3 = 11$ people
    $11 - 4 = 7$ people

Lesson Practice 24A

1. $10 - 7 = 3$
2. $10 - 4 = 6$
3. $10 - 6 = 4$
4. $10 - 3 = 7$
5. $10 - 8 = 2$
6. $10 - 4 = 6$
7. $10 - 5 = 5$
8. $10 - 2 = 8$
9. $10 - 6 = 4$
10. $10 - 0 = 10$
11. $10 - 3 = 7$
12. $10 - 9 = 1$
13. $10 - 6 = 4$
14. $10 - 1 = 9$
15. $10 - 7 = 3$
16. $10 - 3 = 7$ stickers
17. $10 - 4 = 6$ books
18. $10 - 7 = 3$ lollipops

Lesson Practice 24B

1. $10 - 6 = 4$
2. $10 - 2 = 8$
3. $10 - 8 = 2$
4. $10 - 5 = 5$
5. $10 - 3 = 7$
6. $10 - 7 = 3$
7. $10 - 9 = 1$
8. $10 - 4 = 6$
9. $10 - 1 = 9$
10. $10 - 5 = 5$
11. $10 - 7 = 3$
12. $10 - 6 = 4$
13. $10 - 4 = 6$
14. $10 - 0 = 10$
15. $10 - 3 = 7$

16. $10 - 6 = 4$ dollars
17. $10 - 5 = 5$ windows
18. $10 - 8 = 2$ litres

16. $\boxed{4} + 5 = 9$
17. $\boxed{3} + 6 = 9$
18. $\boxed{8} + 1 = 9$
19. $8 + 7 = 15$ pieces
20. $5 + 4 = 9$ calls
    $9 + 9 = 18$ calls

Lesson Practice 24C
1. $10 - 1 = 9$
2. $10 - 3 = 7$
3. $10 - 5 = 5$
4. $10 - 9 = 1$
5. $10 - 7 = 3$
6. $10 - 6 = 4$
7. $10 - 4 = 6$
8. $10 - 8 = 2$
9. $10 - 2 = 8$
10. $10 - 3 = 7$
11. $10 - 0 = 10$
12. $10 - 5 = 5$
13. $10 - 7 = 3$
14. $10 - 6 = 4$
15. $10 - 4 = 6$
16. $10 - 4 = 6$ years
17. $10 - 2 = 8$ toads
18. $10 - 3 = 7$ metres

Systematic Review 24D
1. $10 - 5 = 5$
2. $12 - 6 = 6$
3. $10 - 7 = 3$
4. $17 - 8 = 9$
5. $10 - 3 = 7$
6. $70 - 20 = 50$
7. $10 - 4 = 6$
8. $14 - 7 = 7$
9. $16 - 9 = 7$
10. $10 - 8 = 2$
11. $9 - 7 = 2$
12. $8 + 5 = 13$
13. $2 + 6 = 8$
14. $3 + 4 = 7$
15. $700 + 100 = 800$

Systematic Review 24E
1. $10 - 7 = 3$
2. $8 - 4 = 4$
3. $10 - 6 = 4$
4. $16 - 8 = 8$
5. $10 - 5 = 5$
6. $7 - 5 = 2$
7. $10 - 3 = 7$
8. $400 - 200 = 200$
9. $12 - 8 = 4$
10. $14 - 9 = 5$
11. $10 - 1 = 9$
12. $9 + 6 = 15$
13. $6 + 5 = 11$
14. $8 + 9 = 17$
15. $30 + 50 = 80$
16. $\boxed{5} + 4 = 9$
17. $\boxed{7} + 2 = 9$
18. $\boxed{6} + 3 = 9$
19. $10 - 8 = 2$ students
20. $3 + 1 = 4$ songs
    $4 + 2 = 6$ songs

Systematic Review 24F
1. $10 - 4 = 6$
2. $6 - 3 = 3$
3. $10 - 7 = 3$
4. $9 - 8 = 1$
5. $10 - 6 = 4$
6. $11 - 9 = 2$
7. $10 - 2 = 8$
8. $600 - 400 = 200$

9. $50 - 20 = 30$
10. $4 - 4 = 0$
11. $8 - 7 = 1$
12. $2 + 9 = 11$
13. $5 + 5 = 10$
14. $7 + 6 = 13$
15. $4 + 9 = 13$
16. $\boxed{1} + 8 = 9$
17. $\boxed{9} + 0 = 9$
18. $\boxed{2} + 7 = 9$
19. $9 - 6 = 3$ eggs
20. $5 + 2 = 7$ bird houses
    $9 - 7 = 2$ bird houses

6. $90 - 30 = 60$
7. $900 - 700 = 200$
8. $9 - 9 = 0$
9. $9 - 1 = 8$
10. $9 - 5 = 4$
11. $9 - 8 = 1$
12. $9 - 4 = 5$
13. $9 - 2 = 7$
14. $9 - 3 = 6$
15. $9 - 6 = 3$
16. $9 - 3 = 6$ years
17. $9 - 1 = 8$ sparrows
18. $9 - 5 = 4$ chapters

Lesson Practice 25A

1. $9 - 3 = 6$
2. $9 - 6 = 3$
3. $90 - 40 = 50$
4. $9 - 7 = 2$
5. $900 - 100 = 800$
6. $9 - 9 = 0$
7. $9 - 6 = 3$
8. $9 - 5 = 4$
9. $9 - 7 = 2$
10. $9 - 4 = 5$
11. $9 - 9 = 0$
12. $9 - 3 = 6$
13. $9 - 8 = 1$
14. $9 - 2 = 7$
15. $9 - 5 = 4$
16. $9 - 6 = 3$ dollars
17. $9 - 5 = 4$ Band-Aids
18. $9 - 4 = 5$ gifts

Lesson Practice 25C

1. $9 - 7 = 2$
2. $9 - 5 = 4$
3. $9 - 3 = 6$
4. $90 - 60 = 30$
5. $9 - 0 = 9$
6. $9 - 4 = 5$
7. $900 - 200 = 700$
8. $9 - 1 = 8$
9. $9 - 8 = 1$
10. $9 - 9 = 0$
11. $9 - 5 = 4$
12. $9 - 6 = 3$
13. $9 - 3 = 6$
14. $9 - 4 = 5$
15. $9 - 7 = 2$
16. $9 - 6 = 3$ cows
17. $9 - 4 = 5$ lines
18. $9 - 7 = 2$ dollars

Lesson Practice 25B

1. $9 - 8 = 1$
2. $9 - 4 = 5$
3. $9 - 5 = 4$
4. $9 - 2 = 7$
5. $9 - 6 = 3$

Systematic Review 25D

1. $9 - 6 = 3$
2. $10 - 7 = 3$
3. $9 - 4 = 5$
4. $18 - 9 = 9$

5. $90 - 50 = 40$
6. $10 - 4 = 6$
7. $9 - 3 = 6$
8. $10 - 6 = 4$
9. $8 - 2 = 6$
10. $10 - 5 = 5$
11. $6 - 4 = 2$
12. $9 + 9 = 18$
13. $200 + 300 = 500$
14. $5 + 7 = 12$
15. $6 + 6 = 12$
16. $\boxed{3} + 4 = 7$
17. $\boxed{5} + 3 = 8$
18. $\boxed{4} + 3 = 7$
19. $9 + 8 = 17$ books
20. $6 + 7 = 13$ flowers
    $13 - 8 = 5$ flowers

Systematic Review 25E

1. $9 - 2 = 7$
2. $9 - 5 = 4$
3. $10 - 3 = 7$
4. $14 - 8 = 6$
5. $9 - 3 = 6$
6. $10 - 2 = 8$
7. $13 - 8 = 5$
8. $40 - 20 = 20$
9. $12 - 8 = 4$
10. $16 - 9 = 7$
11. $15 - 8 = 7$
12. $6 + 7 = 13$
13. $50 + 40 = 90$
14. $5 + 6 = 11$
15. $7 + 7 = 14$
16. $\boxed{5} + 3 = 8$
17. $\boxed{4} + 3 = 7$
18. $\boxed{3} + 5 = 8$
19. $9 - 4 = 5$ cards
20. $3 + 6 = 9$ children
    $11 - 9 = 2$ children

Systematic Review 25F

1. $9 - 4 = 5$
2. $10 - 8 = 2$
3. $9 - 6 = 3$
4. $16 - 8 = 8$
5. $10 - 5 = 5$
6. $13 - 9 = 4$
7. $600 - 300 = 300$
8. $8 - 0 = 8$
9. $7 - 1 = 6$
10. $11 - 8 = 3$
11. $10 - 2 = 8$
12. $7 + 9 = 16$
13. $4 + 8 = 12$
14. $400 + 400 = 800$
15. $8 + 5 = 13$
16. $\boxed{4} + 3 = 7$
17. $\boxed{5} + 3 = 8$
18. $\boxed{3} + 4 = 7$
19. $9 + 7 = 16$ insects
20. $4 + 4 = 8$ pieces of fruit now
    $16 - 8 = 8$ pieces of fruit to buy

Lesson Practice 26A

1. $7 - 4 = 3$
2. $8 - 3 = 5$
3. $80 - 50 = 30$
4. $7 - 3 = 4$
5. $8 - 5 = 3$
6. $70 - 40 = 30$
7. $8 - 3 = 5$
8. $7 - 3 = 4$
9. $8 - 5 = 3$
10. $7 - 4 = 3$
11. $8 - 3 = 5$
12. $7 - 3 = 4$
13. eight minus five equals three
14. seven minus four equals three
15. $7 - 3 = 4$ monkeys
16. $8 - 5 = 3$ kittens
17. $7 - 4 = 3$ chores
18. $8 - 3 = 5$ centimetres

Lesson Practice 26B

1. $8 - 3 = 5$
2. $7 - 3 = 4$
3. $7 - 4 = 3$
4. $8 - 5 = 3$
5. $8 - 3 = 5$
6. $70 - 30 = 40$
7. $9 - 3 = 6$
8. $9 - 5 = 4$
9. $700 - 600 = 100$
10. $16 - 8 = 8$
11. $14 - 9 = 5$
12. $10 - 7 = 3$
13. twelve minus six equals six
14. eleven minus nine equals two
15. $7 - 3 = 4$ days
16. $7 - 4 = 3$ bags
17. $8 - 5 = 3$ metres
18. $8 - 3 = 5$ years

Lesson Practice 26C

1. $7 - 3 = 4$
2. $8 - 5 = 3$
3. $80 - 30 = 50$
4. $7 - 4 = 3$
5. $7 - 3 = 4$
6. $800 - 500 = 300$
7. $9 - 7 = 2$
8. $10 - 9 = 1$
9. $17 - 9 = 8$
10. $10 - 8 = 2$
11. $14 - 7 = 7$
12. $5 - 3 = 2$
13. ten minus one equals nine
14. eight minus four equals four
15. $8 - 3 = 5$ nickels
16. $7 - 3 = 4$ girls
17. $8 - 5 = 3$ chores
18. $8 - 3 = 5$ blocks

Systematic Review 26D

1. $8 - 5 = 3$
2. $7 - 4 = 3$
3. $8 - 3 = 5$
4. $7 - 3 = 4$
5. $9 - 4 = 5$
6. $70 - 20 = 50$
7. $5 - 0 = 5$
8. $12 - 9 = 3$
9. $4 - 4 = 0$
10. $10 - 4 = 6$
11. $14 - 8 = 6$
12. $7 + 8 = 15$
13. $500 + 400 = 900$
14. $3 + 2 = 5$
15. $0 + 9 = 9$
16. $\boxed{7} + 4 = 11$
17. $\boxed{8} + 7 = 15$
18. $\boxed{7} + 5 = 12$
19. $8 + 2 = 10$ metres
20. $9 + 4 = 13$ dollars

Systematic Review 26E

1. $7 - 4 = 3$
2. $8 - 3 = 5$
3. $7 - 3 = 4$
4. $8 - 5 = 3$
5. $10 - 5 = 5$
6. $40 - 10 = 30$
7. $500 - 200 = 300$
8. $12 - 8 = 4$
9. $9 - 0 = 9$
10. $16 - 9 = 7$
11. $9 - 8 = 1$
12. $60 + 20 = 80$
13. $7 + 4 = 11$
14. $5 + 6 = 11$
15. $9 + 3 = 12$
16. $\boxed{7} + 9 = 16$
17. $\boxed{6} + 7 = 13$
18. $\boxed{4} + 7 = 11$

19. $9 + 5 = 14$ players
20. $8 + 1 = 9$ steaks
    $9 - 2 = 7$ steaks

13. sixteen minus seven equals nine
14. thirteen minus seven equals six
15. $13 - 7 = 6$ doughnuts
16. $16 - 7 = 9$ bulbs
17. $11 - 7 = 4$ dollars
18. $15 - 7 = 8$ kilometres

Systematic Review 26F

1. $8 - 3 = 5$
2. $8 - 7 = 1$
3. $7 - 3 = 4$
4. $80 - 40 = 40$
5. $9 - 6 = 3$
6. $11 - 8 = 3$
7. $7 - 1 = 6$
8. $10 - 6 = 4$
9. $6 - 4 = 2$
10. $7 - 5 = 2$
11. $15 - 9 = 6$
12. $9 + 6 = 15$
13. $3 + 8 = 11$
14. $400 + 200 = 600$
15. $9 + 8 = 17$
16. $\boxed{7} + 8 = 15$
17. $\boxed{5} + 7 = 12$
18. $\boxed{7} + 6 = 13$
19. $5 + 5 = 10$ calls
20. $6 + 1 = 7$ bagels
    $7 + 6 = 13$ bagels

Lesson Practice 27B

1. $16 - 7 = 9$
2. $11 - 7 = 4$
3. $13 - 7 = 6$
4. $15 - 7 = 8$
5. $12 - 7 = 5$
6. $16 - 7 = 9$
7. $13 - 7 = 6$
8. $10 - 3 = 7$
9. $7 - 4 = 3$
10. $8 - 2 = 6$
11. $13 - 9 = 4$
12. $8 - 5 = 3$
13. fifteen minus seven equals eight
14. eleven minus seven equals four
15. $16 - 7 = 9$ kilometres
16. $12 - 7 = 5$ stories
17. $13 - 7 = 6$ years
18. $15 - 7 = 8$ cents

Lesson Practice 27A

1. $11 - 7 = 4$
2. $13 - 7 = 6$
3. $12 - 7 = 5$
4. $16 - 7 = 9$
5. $15 - 7 = 8$
6. $11 - 7 = 4$
7. $12 - 7 = 5$
8. $16 - 7 = 9$
9. $13 - 7 = 6$
10. $15 - 7 = 8$
11. $12 - 7 = 5$
12. $11 - 7 = 4$

Lesson Practice 27C

1. $15 - 7 = 8$
2. $12 - 7 = 5$
3. $11 - 7 = 4$
4. $13 - 7 = 6$
5. $16 - 7 = 9$
6. $12 - 7 = 5$
7. $11 - 7 = 4$
8. $14 - 7 = 7$
9. $6 - 3 = 3$
10. $13 - 8 = 5$
11. $7 - 3 = 4$
12. $18 - 9 = 9$

13. thirteen minus seven equals six
14. sixteen minus seven equals nine
15. $15 - 7 = 8$ kilograms
16. $12 - 7 = 5$ eggs
17. $16 - 7 = 9$ people
18. $11 - 7 = 4$ kilograms

Systematic Review 27D
1. $12 - 7 = 5$
2. $15 - 7 = 8$
3. $11 - 7 = 4$
4. $13 - 7 = 6$
5. $8 - 6 = 2$
6. $15 - 8 = 7$
7. $80 - 30 = 50$
8. $3 - 0 = 3$
9. $17 - 8 = 9$
10. $16 - 7 = 9$
11. $10 - 2 = 8$
12. $2 + 8 = 10$
13. $3 + 5 = 8$
14. $8 + 6 = 14$
15. $400 + 300 = 700$
16. $\boxed{6} + 5 = 11$
17. $\boxed{7} + 6 = 13$
18. $\boxed{9} + 6 = 15$
19. $3 + 3 = 6$ mice
20. $3 + 2 = 5$ pets
    $5 + 4 = 9$ pets

Systematic Review 27E
1. $13 - 7 = 6$
2. $11 - 7 = 4$
3. $15 - 7 = 8$
4. $12 - 7 = 5$
5. $6 - 2 = 4$
6. $14 - 8 = 6$
7. $70 - 40 = 30$
8. $10 - 6 = 4$

9. $16 - 9 = 7$
10. $11 - 2 = 9$
11. $8 - 4 = 4$
12. $6 + 4 = 10$
13. $7 + 0 = 7$
14. $9 + 8 = 17$
15. $500 + 200 = 700$
16. $\boxed{6} + 8 = 14$
17. $\boxed{5} + 6 = 11$
18. $\boxed{6} + 7 = 13$
19. $6 - 6 = 0$ dollars
20. $18 - 9 = 9$ years old

Systematic Review 27F
1. $11 - 7 = 4$
2. $15 - 7 = 8$
3. $13 - 7 = 6$
4. $16 - 7 = 9$
5. $12 - 7 = 5$
6. $70 - 30 = 40$
7. $10 - 4 = 6$
8. $14 - 7 = 7$
9. $11 - 4 = 7$
10. $50 - 10 = 40$
11. $17 - 8 = 9$
12. $4 + 8 = 12$
13. $9 + 2 = 11$
14. $7 + 9 = 16$
15. $8 + 3 = 11$
16. $\boxed{6} + 9 = 15$
17. $\boxed{8} + 6 = 14$
18. $\boxed{6} + 5 = 11$
19. $3 + 3 = 6$ good ideas
    $6 + 7 = 13$ good ideas
20. $3 + 6 = 9$ gifts bought
    $9 - 2 = 7$ gifts left to wrap

Lesson Practice 28A

1. $14 - 6 = 8$
2. $13 - 6 = 7$
3. $11 - 6 = 5$
4. $15 - 7 = 8$
5. $12 - 6 = 6$
6. $14 - 6 = 8$
7. $13 - 6 = 7$
8. $15 - 6 = 9$
9. $10 - 6 = 4$
10. $14 - 6 = 8$
11. $11 - 6 = 5$
12. $13 - 7 = 6$
13. fifteen minus six equals nine
14. eleven minus six equals five
15. $13 - 6 = 7$ children
16. $14 - 6 = 8$ outfits
17. $15 - 6 = 9$ daffodils
18. $11 - 6 = 5$ peppers

Lesson Practice 28B

1. $11 - 6 = 5$
2. $15 - 6 = 9$
3. $14 - 6 = 8$
4. $13 - 6 = 7$
5. $11 - 6 = 5$
6. $15 - 6 = 9$
7. $9 - 4 = 5$
8. $14 - 6 = 8$
9. $13 - 6 = 7$
10. $13 - 9 = 4$
11. $8 - 3 = 5$
12. $10 - 5 = 5$
13. eight minus five equals three
14. eleven minus eight equals three
15. $14 - 6 = 8$ days
16. $13 - 6 = 7$ kilometres
17. $15 - 6 = 9$ shells
18. $11 - 6 = 5$ chores

Lesson Practice 28C

1. $13 - 6 = 7$
2. $12 - 6 = 6$
3. $15 - 6 = 9$
4. $11 - 6 = 5$
5. $14 - 6 = 8$
6. $13 - 6 = 7$
7. $7 - 5 = 2$
8. $6 - 3 = 3$
9. $15 - 7 = 8$
10. $12 - 8 = 4$
11. $16 - 7 = 9$
12. $6 - 1 = 5$
13. fourteen minus six equals eight
14. nine minus six equals three
15. $11 - 6 = 5$ people
16. $15 - 6 = 9$ balloons
17. $14 - 6 = 8$ dimes
18. $13 - 6 = 7$ apples

Systematic Review 28D

1. $15 - 6 = 9$
2. $11 - 6 = 5$
3. $14 - 6 = 8$
4. $13 - 6 = 7$
5. $10 - 3 = 7$
6. $16 - 7 = 9$
7. $15 - 9 = 6$
8. $10 - 7 = 3$
9. $90 - 50 = 40$
10. $14 - 9 = 5$
11. $15 - 8 = 7$
12. $40 + 30 = 70$
13. $6 + 4 = 10$
14. $8 + 5 = 13$
15. $7 + 7 = 14$
16. $\boxed{5} + 7 = 12$
17. $\boxed{6} + 5 = 11$
18. $\boxed{5} + 9 = 14$
19. $8 - 1 = 7$ donuts
    $7 - 1 = 6$ donuts

20. 9 + 5 = 14 people invited
14 − 7 = 7 people didn't come

Systematic Review 28E

1. 14 − 6 = 8
2. 11 − 6 = 5
3. 13 − 6 = 7
4. 15 − 6 = 9
5. 13 − 7 = 6
6. 17 − 9 = 8
7. 50 − 30 = 20
8. 8 − 6 = 2
9. 12 − 7 = 5
10. 15 − 7 = 8
11. 12 − 9 = 3
12. 3 + 7 = 10
13. 3 + 9 = 12
14. 8 + 6 = 14
15. 30 + 50 = 80
16. ⟦5⟧ + 6 = 11
17. ⟦5⟧ + 8 = 13
18. ⟦7⟧ + 5 = 12
19. 7 + 4 = 11 mosquitoes
11 − 9 = 2 mosquitoes
20. 5 + 8 = 13 things

Systematic Review 28F

1. 11 − 6 = 5
2. 15 − 6 = 9
3. 14 − 6 = 8
4. 13 − 6 = 7
5. 11 − 7 = 4
6. 13 − 8 = 5
7. 500 − 200 = 300
8. 8 − 0 = 8
9. 9 − 5 = 4
10. 10 − 4 = 6
11. 9 − 3 = 6
12. 9 + 2 = 11
13. 7 + 5 = 12

14. 8 + 8 = 16
15. 7 + 8 = 15
16. ⟦8⟧ + 5 = 13
17. ⟦9⟧ + 5 = 14
18. ⟦6⟧ + 5 = 11
19. 7 + 7 = 14 feathers
14 − 9 = 5 feathers
20. 7 + 4 = 11 glasses
11 − 6 = 5 glasses

Lesson Practice 29A

1. 12 − 5 = 7
2. 11 − 5 = 6
3. 13 − 5 = 8
4. 14 − 5 = 9
5. 10 − 5 = 5
6. 11 − 5 = 6
7. 13 − 5 = 8
8. 12 − 5 = 7
9. 14 − 5 = 9
10. 12 − 5 = 7
11. 13 − 5 = 8
12. 11 − 5 = 6
13. fourteen minus five equals nine
14. ten minus five equals five
15. 14 − 5 = 9 dollars
16. 11 − 5 = 6 times
17. 13 − 5 = 8 dollars
18. 12 − 5 = 7 months

Lesson Practice 29B

1. 14 − 5 = 9
2. 12 − 5 = 7
3. 11 − 5 = 6
4. 13 − 5 = 8
5. 11 − 7 = 4
6. 14 − 6 = 8
7. 12 − 5 = 7
8. 14 − 5 = 9

9. $13 - 8 = 5$
10. $10 - 2 = 8$
11. $12 - 5 = 7$
12. $6 - 3 = 3$
13. eleven minus five equals six
14. twelve minus seven equals five
15. $13 - 5 = 8$ metres
16. $14 - 5 = 9$ years old
17. $12 - 5 = 7$ models
18. $11 - 5 = 6$ centimetres

Lesson Practice 29C

1. $13 - 5 = 8$
2. $14 - 5 = 9$
3. $12 - 5 = 7$
4. $11 - 5 = 6$
5. $8 - 4 = 4$
6. $7 - 6 = 1$
7. $8 - 3 = 5$
8. $18 - 9 = 9$
9. $15 - 8 = 7$
10. $12 - 6 = 6$
11. $9 - 3 = 6$
12. $6 - 4 = 2$
13. sixteen minus nine equals seven
14. ten minus six equals four
15. $14 - 5 = 9$ people
16. $12 - 5 = 7$ eggs
17. $11 - 5 = 6$ kilometres
18. $13 - 5 = 8$ dollars

Systematic Review 29D

1. $11 - 5 = 6$
2. $13 - 5 = 8$
3. $12 - 5 = 7$
4. $14 - 5 = 9$
5. $10 - 5 = 5$
6. $13 - 9 = 4$
7. $11 - 6 = 5$
8. $9 - 4 = 5$

9. $80 - 50 = 30$
10. $16 - 7 = 9$
11. $12 - 9 = 3$
12. $6 + 7 = 13$
13. $40 + 40 = 80$
14. $8 + 6 = 14$
15. $3 + 7 = 10$
16. $\boxed{4} + 7 = 11$
17. $\boxed{3} + 9 = 12$
18. $\boxed{9} + 4 = 13$
19. $7 - 5 = 2$ flowers
    $2 + 8 = 10$ flowers
20. $7 + 5 = 12$ hyenas
    $12 - 9 = 3$ hyenas

Systematic Review 29E

1. $12 - 5 = 7$
2. $14 - 5 = 9$
3. $11 - 5 = 6$
4. $13 - 5 = 8$
5. $15 - 6 = 9$
6. $12 - 8 = 4$
7. $60 - 20 = 40$
8. $700 - 400 = 300$
9. $10 - 7 = 3$
10. $17 - 8 = 9$
11. $9 - 6 = 3$
12. $0 + 2 = 2$
13. $9 + 7 = 16$
14. $6 + 3 = 9$
15. $7 + 8 = 15$
16. $\boxed{4} + 8 = 12$
17. $\boxed{8} + 3 = 11$
18. $\boxed{7} + 4 = 11$
19. $2 + 1 = 3$ zoos
    $3 + 5 = 8$ zoos
20. $10 + 6 = 16$ books
    $16 - 8 = 8$ books

Systematic Review 29F

1. $14 - 5 = 9$
2. $11 - 5 = 6$
3. $13 - 5 = 8$
4. $12 - 5 = 7$
5. $7 - 3 = 4$
6. $17 - 9 = 8$
7. $10 - 1 = 9$
8. $13 - 7 = 6$
9. $11 - 8 = 3$
10. $7 - 5 = 2$
11. $15 - 9 = 6$
12. $9 + 8 = 17$
13. $700 + 200 = 900$
14. $8 + 0 = 8$
15. $9 + 9 = 18$
16. $\boxed{4} + 9 = 13$
17. $\boxed{9} + 3 = 12$
18. $\boxed{3} + 8 = 11$
19. $6 + 1 = 7$ hours
    $7 - 4 = 3$ hours
20. $8 + 6 = 14$ times
    $14 - 5 = 9$ times

Lesson Practice 30A

1. $13 - 4 = 9$
2. $12 - 4 = 8$
3. $11 - 4 = 7$
4. $11 - 3 = 8$
5. $12 - 3 = 9$
6. $12 - 4 = 8$
7. $12 - 3 = 9$
8. $13 - 4 = 9$
9. $11 - 3 = 8$
10. $13 - 4 = 9$
11. $11 - 4 = 7$
12. $12 - 3 = 9$
13. eleven minus three equals eight
14. twelve minus four equals eight
15. $11 - 4 = 7$ students
16. $13 - 4 = 9$ days

17. $12 - 4 = 8$ years
18. $12 - 3 = 9$ lilies

Lesson Practice 30B

1. $11 - 3 = 8$
2. $13 - 4 = 9$
3. $12 - 3 = 9$
4. $12 - 4 = 8$
5. $11 - 4 = 7$
6. $13 - 4 = 9$
7. $13 - 5 = 8$
8. $12 - 4 = 8$
9. $12 - 3 = 9$
10. $12 - 5 = 7$
11. $11 - 4 = 7$
12. $11 - 3 = 8$
13. fourteen minus nine equals five
14. eleven minus five equals six
15. $12 - 4 = 8$ metres
16. $11 - 3 = 8$ apples
17. $13 - 4 = 9$ litres
18. $11 - 4 = 7$ kilometres

Lesson Practice 30C

1. $12 - 4 = 8$
2. $11 - 3 = 9$
3. $11 - 4 = 7$
4. $12 - 3 = 9$
5. $13 - 4 = 9$
6. $14 - 5 = 9$
7. $10 - 8 = 2$
8. $11 - 9 = 2$
9. $14 - 8 = 6$
10. $11 - 4 = 7$
11. $11 - 3 = 8$
12. $12 - 4 = 8$
13. thirteen minus four equals nine
14. twelve minus three equals nine
15. $11 - 3 = 8$ girls
16. $12 - 4 = 8$ years

17. $12 - 3 = 9$ dimes
18. $13 - 4 = 9$ spaces

Systematic Review 30D
1. $12 - 3 = 9$
2. $11 - 4 = 7$
3. $13 - 4 = 9$
4. $11 - 3 = 8$
5. $12 - 4 = 8$
6. $16 - 8 = 8$
7. $10 - 3 = 7$
8. $9 - 7 = 2$
9. $3 - 3 = 0$
10. $8 - 4 = 4$
11. $11 - 5 = 6$
12. $13 - 6 = 7$
13. $9 - 5 = 4$
14. $15 - 6 = 9$
15. $2 + 3 = 5$
16. $9 + 1 = 10$
17. $60 + 30 = 90$
18. $200 + 700 = 900$
19. $11 - 4 = 7$ trees
20. $7 + 8 = 15$ pictures
    $15 - 9 = 6$ pictures

Systematic Review 30E
1. $11 - 4 = 7$
2. $13 - 4 = 9$
3. $11 - 3 = 8$
4. $12 - 4 = 8$
5. $12 - 3 = 9$
6. $14 - 7 = 7$
7. $6 - 3 = 3$
8. $13 - 5 = 8$
9. $14 - 6 = 8$
10. $10 - 7 = 3$
11. $12 - 8 = 4$
12. $14 - 5 = 9$
13. $90 - 40 = 50$

14. $8 - 5 = 3$
15. $4 + 7 = 11$
16. $8 + 3 = 11$
17. $9 + 4 = 13$
18. $6 + 5 = 11$
19. $15 - 9 = 6$ math facts
20. $4 + 4 = 8$ bouquets
    $8 - 3 = 5$ bouquets

Systematic Review 30F
1. $13 - 4 = 9$
2. $12 - 4 = 8$
3. $12 - 3 = 9$
4. $11 - 4 = 7$
5. $11 - 3 = 8$
6. $12 - 5 = 7$
7. $11 - 6 = 5$
8. $13 - 8 = 5$
9. $10 - 4 = 6$
10. $9 - 3 = 6$
11. $12 - 7 = 5$
12. $7 - 4 = 3$
13. $17 - 9 = 8$
14. $15 - 7 = 8$
15. $8 + 4 = 12$
16. $30 + 40 = 70$
17. $7 + 9 = 16$
18. $5 + 7 = 12$
19. $5 + 6 = 11$ jelly beans
    $11 - 7 = 4$ jelly beans
20. $12 - 7 = 5$ bananas
    $5 + 2 = 7$ bananas

Appendix A-1
1. :10
2. :20
3. :40
4. :35
5. :50
6. :45

Appendix A-2
1. : 05
2. : 25
3. : 55
4. : 50
5. : 30
6. : 15

Appendix B-1
1. 9 : 00
2. 7 : 00
3. 11 : 00
4. 1 : 00

Appendix B-2
1. 8 : 00
2. 2 : 00
3. 12 : 00
4. 4 : 00

Appendix B-3
1. 11 : 30
2. 5 : 45
3. 3 : 40
4. 12 : 25

Appendix B-4
1. 5 : 50
2. 2 : 40
3. 7 : 10
4. 4 : 15

Test Solutions

Test 1

1. 5 hundreds, 3 tens, and 6 units;
   five hundred thirty-six
2. 129;
   one hundred twenty-nine
3. 1 hundred, 4 tens, and 1 unit;
   one hundred forty-one
4. 3 hundreds and 9 tens;
   three hundred ninety
5. 9
6. 9

Test 2

1. 0, 1, 2, 3, 4, 5, 6, 7, 8, 9, 10, 11,
   12, 13, 14, 15, 16, 17, 18, 19, 20
2. 0, 1, 2, 3, 4, 5, 6, 7, 8, 9, 10, 11,
   12, 13, 14, 15, 16, 17, 18, 19, 20
3. 263;
   two hundred sixty-three
4. 1 hundred, 5 tens, and 7 units;
   one hundred fifty-seven
5. 3 tens and 8 units;
   thirty-eight

Test 3

1. (4)
2. (7)
3. (5)
4. (6)
5. brown
6. 326;
   three hundred twenty-six
7. 0, 1, 2, 3, 4, 5, 6, 7, 8, 9, 10, 11,
   12. 13. 14. 15. 16. 17. 18. 19. 20

Test 4

1. $0 + 1 = 1$
2. $8 + 0 = 8$
3. $0 + 6 = 6$
4. $5 + 0 = 5$
5. $4 + 0 = 4$
6. $0 + 3 = 3$
7. $0 + 0 = 0$
8. $0 + 7 = 7$
9. $2 + 0 = 2$
10. $1 + 0 = 1$
11. $3 + 0 = 3$
12. $0 + 5 = 5$
13. 3 hundreds and 5 tens;
    three hundred fifty
14. 1 hundred and 2 units;
    one hundred two
15. light green
16. $6 + 0 = 6$

Test 5

1. $5 + 1 = 6$
2. $4 + 1 = 5$
3. $1 + 8 = 9$
4. $2 + 1 = 3$
5. $7 + 1 = 8$
6. $1 + 3 = 4$
7. $1 + 1 = 2$
8. $1 + 9 = 10$
9. $6 + 1 = 7$
10. $0 + 5 = 5$
11. $8 + 0 = 8$
12. $0 + 2 = 2$
13. 194;
    one hundred ninety-four

14. 2 hundreds, 1 ten, and 4 units
    two hundred fourteen
15. 5 + 1 = 6 children

Test 6

1. 0 1 2 3 4 5 6 7 8 9
    10 11 12 13 14 15 16 17 18 19
    20 21 22 23 24 25 26 27 28 29
    30 31 32 33 34 35 36 37 38 39
    40 41 42 43 44 45 46 47 48 49
    50 51 52 53 54 55 56 57 58 59
    60 61 62 63 64 65 66 67 68 69
    70 71 72 73 74 75 76 77 78 79
    80 81 82 83 84 85 86 87 88 89
    90 91 92 93 94 95 96 97 98 99
    100
2. 10, 20, 30, 40, 50, 60, 70, 80, 90, 100
3. 1 + 6 = 7
4. 5 + 1 = 6
5. 9 + 0 = 9
6. 1 + 8 = 9

Test 7

1. 1 + 2 = 3
2. 2 + 4 = 6
3. 20 + 20 = 40
4. 100 + 100 = 200
5. 6 + 2 = 8
6. 5 + 2 = 7
7. 2 + 7 = 9
8. 4 + 2 = 6
9. 2 + 3 = 5
10. 2 + 6 = 8
11. 0 + 2 = 2
12. 1 + 7 = 8
13. 3 + 0 = 3
14. 6 + 1 = 7
15. 9 + 1 = 10
16. 0 + 4 = 4
17. 1 + 2 = 3
18. 3 + 2 = 5 pencils

Test 8

1. $\boxed{0}$ + 1 = 1
2. $\boxed{4}$ + 0 = 4
3. $\boxed{0}$ + 2 = 2
4. $\boxed{8}$ + 0 = 8
5. $\boxed{3}$ + 2 = 5
6. $\boxed{6}$ + 1 = 7
7. $\boxed{1}$ + 2 = 3
8. $\boxed{5}$ + 1 = 6
9. $\boxed{0}$ + 0 = 0
10. $\boxed{8}$ + 1 = 9
11. $\boxed{1}$ + 0 = 1
12. $\boxed{2}$ + 2 = 4
13. 6 + 2 = 8
14. 7 + 1 = 8
15. 30 + 20 = 50
16. 9 + 0 = 9
17. $\boxed{2}$ + 3 = 5 cars
18. $\boxed{1}$ + 8 = 9 players

Test 9

1. 0 + 9 = 9
2. 9 + 7 = 16
3. 6 + 9 = 15
4. 9 + 9 = 18
5. 9 + 2 = 11
6. 3 + 9 = 12
7. 9 + 1 = 10
8. 8 + 9 = 17
9. 9 + 7 = 16
10. 4 + 9 = 13
11. 6 + 1 = 7
12. 7 + 2 = 9
13. $\boxed{2}$ + 9 = 11
14. $\boxed{4}$ + 2 = 6
15. $\boxed{3}$ + 1 = 4

16. 10, 20, 30, 40, 50, 60, 70, 80, 90, 100
17. 9 + 8 = 17 books
18. 6 + [2] = 8 dollars

Test 10

1. 8 + 8 = 16
2. 8 + 5 = 13
3. 0 + 8 = 8
4. 2 + 8 = 10
5. 8 + 6 = 14
6. 8 + 3 = 11
7. 80 + 10 = 90
8. 7 + 8 = 15
9. 1 + 7 = 8
10. 8 + 9 = 17
11. 2 + 5 = 7
12. 9 + 7 = 16
13. 1 + 3 = 4
14. 9 + 6 = 15
15. 4 + 9 = 13
16. 7 + 2 = 9
17. [8] + 7 = 15
18. [9] + 9 = 18
19. 8 + 5 = 13 kilometres
20. [8] + 9 = 17 beads

Unit Test I

1. 7 + 9 = 16
2. 2 + 2 = 4
3. 4 + 9 = 13
4. 2 + 5 = 7
5. 6 + 2 = 8
6. 8 + 7 = 15
7. 20 + 10 = 30
8. 8 + 0 = 8
9. 2 + 9 = 11
10. 9 + 9 = 18
11. 70 + 20 = 90
12. 100 + 800 = 900

13. 5 + 8 = 13
14. 8 + 4 = 12
15. 8 + 8 = 16
16. 2 + 4 = 6
17. 8 + 6 = 14
18. 6 + 9 = 15
19. 2 + 3 = 5
20. 9 + 5 = 14
21. 2 + 8 = 10
22. 9 + 9 = 18
23. 3 + 9 = 12
24. 9 + 8 = 17
25. [8] + 7 = 15
26. [9] + 9 = 18
27. [9] + 8 = 17
28. 346;
   three hundred forty-six
29. 0, 1, 2, 3, 4, 5, 6, 7, 8, 9, 10, 11,
   12, 13, 14, 15, 16, 17, 18, 19, 20
30. 10, 20, 30, 40, 50, 60, 70, 80, 90, 100
31. 8 + 3 = 11 birds
32. 5 + 1 = 6 pennies

Test 11

1. 4
2. 4
3. 6
4. 4
5. 9 + 8 = 17
6. 8 + 5 = 13
7. 2 + 7 = 9
8. 40 + 20 = 60
9. 3 + 0 = 3
10. 4 + 2 = 6
11. 9 + 9 = 18
12. 6 + 2 = 8
13. [6] + 8 = 14
14. [5] + 2 = 7
15. 2, 4, 6, 8, 10, 12, 14, 16, 18, 20

Test 12

1. $8 + 8 = 16$
2. $5 + 5 = 10$
3. $30 + 30 = 60$
4. $4 + 4 = 8$
5. $6 + 6 = 12$
6. $9 + 9 = 18$
7. $7 + 7 = 14$
8. $2 + 2 = 4$
9. $5 + 8 = 13$
10. $9 + 4 = 13$
11. $3 + 2 = 5$
12. $6 + 9 = 15$
13. $\boxed{9} + 9 = 18$
14. $\boxed{7} + 8 = 15$
15. $\boxed{9} + 2 = 11$
16. 3
17. 4
18. $4 + 4 = 8$ fish
19. $6 + \boxed{9} = 15$ questions
20. $7 + 7 = 14$ chores

Test 13

1. 3
2. 2
3. 3
4. 4
5. $6 + 6 = 12$
6. $3 + 3 = 6$
7. $7 + 7 = 14$
8. $20 + 40 = 60$
9. $9 + 0 = 9$
10. $7 + 1 = 8$
11. $8 + 9 = 17$
12. $5 + 8 = 13$
13. $\boxed{6} + 9 = 15$
14. $4 + \boxed{4} = 8$
15. 4
16. 5, 10, 15, 20, 25, 30, 35, 40, 45, 50

Test 14

1. $50 + 40 = 90$
2. $8 + 7 = 15$
3. $1 + 2 = 3$
4. $6 + 7 = 13$
5. $2 + 3 = 5$
6. $5 + 6 = 11$
7. $8 + 9 = 17$
8. $400 + 300 = 700$
9. $7 + 7 = 14$
10. $8 + 3 = 11$
11. $6 + 6 = 12$
12. $9 + 5 = 14$
13. three plus two equals five
14. two plus two equals four
15. square
16. circle
17. $5 + 5 = 10$ toes
18. $5 + 1 = 6$ brothers and sisters
    $6 + 1 = 7$ children

Test 15

1. $6 + 4 = 10$
2. $9 + 7 = 16$
3. $10 + 20 = 30$
4. $5 + 5 = 10$
5. $9 + 1 = 10$
6. $6 + 8 = 14$
7. $8 + 2 = 10$
8. $8 + 8 = 16$
9. $7 + 3 = 10$
10. $3 + 4 = 7$
11. $5 + 2 = 7$
12. $6 + 4 = 10$
13. $5 + 6 = 11$
14. $7 + 8 = 15$
15. $9 + 5 = 14$
16. $7 + 6 = 13$
17. $\boxed{4} + 6 = 10$

18. $\boxed{5} + 5 = 10$
19. $\boxed{7} + 3 = 10$
20. $8 + \boxed{2} = 10$ toys

Test 16
1. $2 + 7 = 9$
2. $5 + 5 = 10$
3. $10 + 80 = 90$
4. $6 + 3 = 9$
5. $7 + 8 = 15$
6. $5 + 4 = 9$
7. $6 + 6 = 12$
8. $5 + 9 = 14$
9. $8 + 1 = 9$
10. $4 + 4 = 8$
11. $8 + 4 = 12$
12. $5 + \boxed{4} = 9$
13. $6 + \boxed{3} = 9$
14. $7 + \boxed{2} = 9$
15. square
16. circle
17. rectangle
18. triangle
19. $4 + \boxed{5} = 9$ planets
20. $60 + 30 = 90$ pennies

Test 17
1. $30 + 50 = 80$
2. $4 + 7 = 11$
3. $7 + 5 = 12$
4. $5 + 4 = 9$
5. $5 + 7 = 12$
6. $7 + 3 = 10$
7. $200 + 200 = 400$
8. $8 + 7 = 15$
9. $5 + 5 = 10$
10. $9 + 9 = 18$

11. $6 + 4 = 10$
12. $3 + 8 = 11$
13. $6 + 3 = 9$
14. $8 + 5 = 13$
15. $4 + \boxed{7} = 11$
16. $7 + \boxed{5} = 12$
17. $3 + \boxed{5} = 8$
18. $6 + 5 = 11$ balloons
19. $4 + 3 = 7$ birds
20. 5, 10, 15, 20, 25, 30, 35, 40, 45, 50

Unit Test II
1. $9 + 2 = 11$
2. $3 + 3 = 6$
3. $7 + 6 = 13$
4. $3 + 5 = 8$
5. $5 + 1 = 6$
6. $2 + 7 = 9$
7. $40 + 10 = 50$
8. $2 + 4 = 6$
9. $2 + 2 = 4$
10. $2 + 8 = 10$
11. $50 + 20 = 70$
12. $400 + 500 = 900$
13. $8 + 6 = 14$
14. $9 + 7 = 16$
15. $40 + 30 = 70$
16. $300 + 100 = 400$
17. $8 + 3 = 11$
18. $6 + 9 = 15$
19. $6 + 6 = 12$
20. $8 + 4 = 12$
21. $0 + 6 = 6$
22. $7 + 7 = 14$
23. $5 + 6 = 11$
24. $8 + 5 = 13$
25. $7 + 3 = 10$
26. $9 + 9 = 18$
27. $9 + 4 = 13$
28. $7 + 8 = 15$
29. $4 + 4 = 8$

30.	$2 + 3 = 5$
31.	$20 + 30 = 50$
32.	$7 + 5 = 12$
33.	$0 + 9 = 9$
34.	$5 + 5 = 10$
35.	$10 + 10 = 20$
36.	$600 + 300 = 900$
37.	$8 + 0 = 8$
38.	$3 + 9 = 12$
39.	$20 + 60 = 80$
40.	$300 + 300 = 600$
41.	$8 + 8 = 16$
42.	$4 + 7 = 11$
43.	$9 + 8 = 17$
44.	$4 + 6 = 10$
45.	rectangle
46.	triangle
47.	square
48.	circle

Test 18

1. have 2 (orange)
2. owe 10 (dark blue)
3. have 3 (pink)
4. have 5 (light blue)
5. have 6 (violet)
6. owe 8 (brown)
7. $4 + 7 = 11$
8. $6 + 5 = 11$
9. $5 + 4 = 9$
10. $600 + 300 = 900$
11. $\boxed{7} + 0 = 7$
12. $\boxed{2} + 1 = 3$
13. $\boxed{6} + 0 = 6$
14. $\boxed{8} + 1 = 9$
15. $\boxed{5} + 3 = 8$
16. $\boxed{4} + 6 = 10$

Test 19

1. $4 - 1 = 3$
2. $6 - 5 = 1$
3. $8 - 8 = 0$
4. $1 - 0 = 1$
5. $2 - 1 = 1$
6. $4 - 3 = 1$
7. $7 - 0 = 7$
8. $9 - 1 = 8$
9. $5 - 4 = 1$
10. $9 - 8 = 1$
11. $6 - 6 = 0$
12. $10 - 1 = 9$
13. $7 - 6 = 1$
14. $6 - 1 = 5$
15. $3 - 3 = 0$
16. $0 - 0 = 0$
17. $\boxed{0} + 7 = 7$
18. $\boxed{2} + 1 = 3$
19. ten minus one equals nine
20. $4 - 0 = 4$ dimes

Test 20

1. $9 - 2 = 7$
2. $8 - 6 = 2$
3. $3 - 2 = 1$
4. $9 - 7 = 2$
5. $5 - 2 = 3$
6. $6 - 4 = 2$
7. $7 - 2 = 5$
8. $7 - 5 = 2$
9. $6 - 2 = 4$
10. $10 - 8 = 2$
11. $2 - 2 = 0$
12. $7 - 1 = 6$
13. $7 + 9 = 16$
14. $9 + 2 = 11$
15. $4 + 9 = 13$
16. $9 + 9 = 18$
17. $\boxed{9} + 5 = 14$
18. $\boxed{9} + 8 = 17$

19. 8 – 2 = 6 children
20. 7 – 5 = 2 points

Test 21
1. 11 – 9 = 2
2. 10 – 9 = 1
3. 14 – 9 = 5
4. 17 – 9 = 8
5. 12 – 9 = 3
6. 13 – 9 = 4
7. 18 – 9 = 9
8. 16 – 9 = 7
9. 15 – 9 = 6
10. 9 – 9 = 0
11. 9 – 2 = 7
12. 8 – 6 = 2
13. 5 + 8 = 13
14. 8 + 7 = 15
15. 4 + 8 = 12
16. 800 + 100 = 900
17. $\boxed{8}$ + 6 = 14
18. $\boxed{3}$ + 8 = 11
19. 11 – 2 = 9 cars
20. 5 – 3 = 2 dollars

Test 22
1. 12 – 8 = 4
2. 15 – 8 = 7
3. 13 – 8 = 5
4. 14 – 8 = 6
5. 16 – 8 = 8
6. 10 – 8 = 2
7. 17 – 8 = 9
8. 9 – 8 = 1
9. 15 – 8 = 7
10. 12 – 9 = 3
11. 16 – 9 = 7
12. 14 – 9 = 5
13. 4 + 4 = 8

14. 7 + 7 = 14
15. 6 + 6 = 12
16. 300 + 300 = 600
17. $\boxed{7}$ + 2 = 9
18. $\boxed{6}$ + 1 = 7
19. 11 – 8 = 3 chapters
20. 17 – 8 = 9 dollars

Test 23
1. 10 – 5 = 5
2. 2 – 1 = 1
3. 14 – 7 = 7
4. 60 – 30 = 30
5. 4 – 2 = 2
6. 16 – 8 = 8
7. 12 – 6 = 6
8. 8 – 4 = 4
9. 18 – 9 = 9
10. 17 – 8 = 9
11. 12 – 8 = 4
12. 15 – 9 = 6
13. 4 + 5 = 9
14. 9 + 1 = 10
15. 3 + 7 = 10
16. 8 + 2 = 10
17. $\boxed{5}$ + 5 = 10
18. $\boxed{7}$ + 9 = 16
19. 6 – 3 = 3 hours
20. 12 – 6 = 6 kilometre

Test 24
1. 10 – 3 = 7
2. 10 – 5 = 5
3. 10 – 2 = 8
4. 10 – 4 = 6
5. 10 – 6 = 4
6. 10 – 8 = 2
7. 10 – 7 = 3
8. 10 – 1 = 9

9. $16 - 8 = 8$
10. $6 - 3 = 3$
11. $14 - 7 = 7$
12. $18 - 9 = 9$
13. $5 + 4 = 9$
14. $7 + 3 = 10$
15. $2 + 7 = 9$
16. $3 + 6 = 9$
17. $\boxed{8} + 1 = 9$
18. $\boxed{4} + 5 = 9$
19. $10 - 4 = 6$ years
20. $10 - 7 = 3$ cards

Unit Test III

1. $13 - 9 = 4$
2. $11 - 8 = 3$
3. $11 - 9 = 2$
4. $14 - 9 = 5$
5. $3 - 1 = 2$
6. $8 - 4 = 4$
7. $7 - 1 = 6$
8. $4 - 0 = 4$
9. $6 - 2 = 4$
10. $9 - 9 = 0$
11. $9 - 8 = 1$
12. $10 - 5 = 5$
13. $3 - 2 = 1$
14. $7 - 2 = 5$
15. $15 - 9 = 6$
16. $2 - 1 = 1$
17. $16 - 9 = 7$
18. $6 - 3 = 3$
19. $10 - 9 = 1$
20. $8 - 2 = 6$
21. $18 - 9 = 9$
22. $5 - 1 = 4$
23. $17 - 8 = 9$
24. $13 - 8 = 5$
25. $7 - 5 = 2$
26. $8 - 7 = 1$
27. $17 - 9 = 8$

28. $14 - 8 = 6$
29. $5 - 3 = 2$
30. $0 - 0 = 0$
31. $9 - 2 = 7$
32. $7 - 6 = 1$
33. $14 - 7 = 7$
34. $12 - 9 = 3$
35. $6 - 4 = 2$
36. $12 - 8 = 4$
37. $6 - 5 = 1$
38. $16 - 8 = 8$
39. $5 - 4 = 1$
40. $2 - 2 = 0$
41. $6 - 0 = 6$
42. $8 - 8 = 0$
43. $8 - 6 = 2$
44. $12 - 6 = 6$
45. $4 - 3 = 1$
46. $9 - 7 = 2$
47. $13 - 8 = 5$
48. $7 - 0 = 7$

Test 25

1. $9 - 4 = 5$
2. $9 - 7 = 2$
3. $9 - 6 = 3$
4. $9 - 0 = 9$
5. $9 - 2 = 7$
6. $9 - 3 = 6$
7. $9 - 1 = 8$
8. $9 - 8 = 1$
9. $10 - 6 = 4$
10. $16 - 8 = 8$
11. $10 - 7 = 3$
12. $14 - 7 = 7$
13. $4 + 3 = 7$
14. $3 + 5 = 8$
15. $8 + 5 = 13$
16. $9 + 4 = 13$
17. $\boxed{4} + 1 = 5$
18. $\boxed{4} + 3 = 7$

19. 9 − 4 = 5 people
20. 9 − 6 = 3 people

14. 6 + 9 = 15
15. 8 + 6 = 14
16. 6 + 7 = 13
17. $\boxed{7}$ + 4 = 11
18. $\boxed{9}$ + 9 = 18
19. 15 − 7 = 8 dollars
20. 13 − 7 = 6 birds

Test 26
1. 7 − 3 = 4
2. 8 − 5 = 3
3. 7 − 4 = 3
4. 8 − 3 = 5
5. 9 − 5 = 4
6. 9 − 6 = 3
7. 15 − 8 = 7
8. 70 − 30 = 40
9. 12 − 9 = 3
10. 17 − 8 = 9
11. 14 − 7 = 7
12. 9 − 2 = 7
13. 7 + 4 = 11
14. 6 + 7 = 13
15. 7 + 5 = 12
16. 9 + 7 = 16
17. $\boxed{8}$ + 7 = 15
18. $\boxed{5}$ + 3 = 8
19. 7 − 4 = 3 centimetres
20. 8 − 3 = 5 years old

Test 27
1. 16 − 7 = 9
2. 13 − 7 = 6
3. 15 − 7 = 8
4. 11 − 7 = 4
5. 12 − 7 = 5
6. 7 − 3 = 4
7. 8 − 5 = 3
8. 70 − 40 = 30
9. 8 − 3 = 5
10. 9 − 5 = 4
11. 10 − 6 = 4
12. 16 − 8 = 8
13. 5 + 6 = 11

Test 28
1. 13 − 6 = 7
2. 15 − 6 = 9
3. 11 − 6 = 5
4. 14 − 6 = 8
5. 15 − 7 = 8
6. 8 − 3 = 5
7. 13 − 7 = 6
8. 70 − 30 = 40
9. 9 − 7 = 2
10. 8 − 1 = 7
11. 15 − 9 = 6
12. 11 − 8 = 3
13. 7 + 5 = 12
14. 5 + 9 = 14
15. 8 + 5 = 13
16. 6 + 5 = 11
17. $\boxed{6}$ + 6 = 12
18. $\boxed{9}$ + 4 = 13
19. 11 − 6 = 5 plates
20. 13 − 6 = 7 toys

Test 29
1. 14 − 5 = 9
2. 12 − 5 = 7
3. 13 − 5 = 8
4. 11 − 5 = 6
5. 13 − 6 = 7
6. 12 − 7 = 5
7. 11 − 6 = 5
8. 40 − 20 = 20

9. $16 - 7 = 9$
10. $14 - 6 = 8$
11. $13 - 7 = 6$
12. $15 - 6 = 9$
13. $7 + 4 = 11$
14. $4 + 9 = 13$
15. $9 + 3 = 12$
16. $8 + 3 = 11$
17. $\boxed{5} + 6 = 11$
18. $\boxed{4} + 8 = 12$
19. $12 - 5 = 7$ words
20. $14 - 5 = 9$ pages

Test 30

1. $12 - 4 = 8$
2. $11 - 3 = 8$
3. $13 - 4 = 9$
4. $12 - 3 = 9$
5. $11 - 4 = 7$
6. $12 - 5 = 7$
7. $11 - 7 = 4$
8. $80 - 50 = 30$
9. $11 - 5 = 6$
10. $15 - 7 = 8$
11. $14 - 6 = 8$
12. $12 - 7 = 5$
13. $13 - 5 = 8$
14. $15 - 6 = 9$
15. $8 + 4 = 12$
16. $6 + 6 = 12$
17. $7 + 7 = 14$
18. $9 + 2 = 11$
19. $13 - 5 = 8$ answers
20. $11 - 3 = 8$ cookies

Unit Test IV

1. $9 - 4 = 5$
2. $7 - 4 = 3$
3. $11 - 3 = 8$
4. $11 - 6 = 5$

5. $13 - 7 = 6$
6. $12 - 7 = 5$
7. $13 - 5 = 8$
8. $11 - 4 = 7$
9. $9 - 6 = 3$
10. $7 - 3 = 4$
11. $11 - 5 = 6$
12. $13 - 6 = 7$
13. $12 - 4 = 8$
14. $8 - 3 = 5$
15. $8 - 5 = 3$
16. $11 - 7 = 4$
17. $12 - 3 = 9$
18. $15 - 7 = 8$
19. $14 - 5 = 9$
20. $9 - 3 = 6$
21. $15 - 6 = 9$
22. $16 - 7 = 9$
23. $9 - 5 = 4$
24. $14 - 6 = 8$
25. $12 - 5 = 7$
26. $13 - 4 = 9$

Final Test

1. $10 - 3 = 7$
2. $7 + 3 = 10$
3. $8 - 4 = 4$
4. $4 + 7 = 11$
5. $9 - 6 = 3$
6. $9 + 9 = 18$
7. $12 - 7 = 5$
8. $8 + 7 = 15$
9. $15 - 9 = 6$
10. $12 - 4 = 8$
11. $5 + 3 = 8$
12. $13 - 6 = 7$
13. $10 - 5 = 5$
14. $7 + 6 = 13$
15. $3 + 6 = 9$
16. $11 - 8 = 3$
17. $8 + 5 = 13$
18. $4 + 9 = 13$

19. $17 - 9 = 8$
20. $14 - 5 = 9$
21. $3 + 8 = 11$
22. $13 - 9 = 4$
23. $5 + 7 = 12$
24. $16 - 7 = 9$
25. $9 + 3 = 12$
26. $11 - 6 = 5$
27. $15 - 8 = 7$
28. $7 + 4 = 11$
29. $5 + 6 = 11$
30. $8 + 7 = 15$

Glossary

A-C

Addend - one of the numbers being added in an addition problem

Associative property - the addends in an addition problem may be regrouped without affecting the sum

Circle - a line drawn around a point with every part the same distance from the centre

Commutative property - the order of the addends in an addition problem may be changed without changing the sum

Corollary - a statement written in a different form that is true because the original statement is true

D-M

Decimal system - our system of numbers that is based on 10

Difference - the answer to a subtraction problem

Equation - a number sentence where one side is equal to the other side

Hundreds - the third place value in the decimal system starting from the right

Minuend - the first number in a subtraction problem

Minus - take away, subtract

P-S

Place value - the position of a number that tells what value it is assigned

Plus - add

Rectangle - a shape with four "square corners," or right angles

Skip counting - counting by groups of numbers, as "by fives" or "by tens"

Square - a rectangle with all four sides the same length. In this book we treat squares and rectangles as two different shapes.

Subtrahend - the second number in a subtraction problem

Sum - the answer to an addition problem

T-Z

Tens - the second place value in the decimal system starting from the right

Triangle - a shape with three sides

Units - the first place value in the decimal system starting from the right

X - stands for an unknown number in an equation

Master Index for General Math

This index lists the levels at which main topics are presented in the Canadian instruction manuals for *Primer* through *Zeta*. For more detail, see the description of each level at www.mathusee.ca. (Many of these topics are also reviewed in subsequent student books.)

Alpha Index